ion

# Five Minutes To Better
# Reading Skills™

A PHONETIC APPROACH TO IMPROVE READING FLUENCY

*Instructor Edition*

Bonnie Terry, M.Ed., BCET



**Bonnie Terry Learning**
238 Poet Smith Dr., Auburn, CA, 95603
www.bonnieterrylearning.com



Printed in the United States of America
ISBN 978-1-891106-14-9

*Inside*

Five Minutes To Better

# Reading Skills™

---

## Overview

Reading fluency drills improve reading speed, accuracy, and comprehension, as well as writing skills. This system can be used with an adult working with a single student, an adult and small reading group, or even by an older student or adult on their own.

## Organization of the Drills

The drills are organized according to phonic rules and letter combinations that are used in reading. Each drill builds upon prior drills, providing continual review and mastery of all concepts. In the Reading Drills, the first sets of words have extra space between the letters, highlighting or emphasizing the letter or letter combination being studied. In the Advanced Drills, the first sets of words have extra space between each syllable. The extra spacing helps improve several areas of visual processing, including visual closure.

Every student, no matter their age, should begin with Drill 1. When the student reaches their mastery goal for Drill 1, they advance to Drill 2, and so on.

## Appropriate Ages to Use the Drills

These drills may be used from 1st grade through adult to develop smoother, more fluent reading. Drills may also be repeated year after year, increasing the words-per-minute mastery target goals as appropriate.

## Sections

› Section 1: Reading Fluency and Research
› Section 2: Directions and Tips for Mastery
› Section 3: Daily Progress and Mastery Charts
› Section 4: Reading Drills
› Section 5: Advanced Reading Drills

The Student Edition contains the reading drills only. The Instructor Edition contains the daily charts, mastery charts, and reading drills. Student drill page numbers coincide with the instructor drill page numbers. All material is copyrighted. The daily charts and mastery charts are for your use only. **These are the only pages you have permission to copy.**

# Table of Contents

**Advanced Reading Drills**

Section 1:

# About Reading Fluency

# What is Reading Fluency?

Reading fluency is the speed and accuracy of reading without conscious attention to the mechanics of reading. Fluent readers read without even thinking about the reading process. They find reading easy and automatic. In other words, they retrieve words automatically. Studies show that slow, single-word reading leads to poor comprehension and frustration. If a student can't read rapidly, they can't hold large pieces of language or text in meaning.

Fluent reading is critical to improving reading skills. Fluency forms the bridge between decoding and comprehension. It is acquired word by word. A student needs to have a minimum of four correct readings of an individual word to recognize it automatically.

Fluency improves with fluency training. No matter a person's reading level or reading challenges, fluency training is one of the most beneficial strategies you can do. It requires little time and minimal experience. While fluency training is important for everyone, it is critical for those with reading problems or dyslexia. In fact, Sally Shaywitz, author of *Overcoming Dyslexia* states, "I urge parents of dyslexic children to make fluency training (repeated oral reading) their number one priority."

### Reading Challenges

Studies show that slow, single-word reading leads to poor comprehension and frustration. If a student can't read rapidly, they typically have difficulty sounding out words, focusing, and attending to reading content. They can't hold large pieces of language or text in meaning.

Other issues may include:

- People who know how to read, but read slowly and skip, omit, repeat or mispronounce words may actually have visual tracking difficulties.
- People who read aloud accurately but slowly, may be slow processors.
- Learning disabilities, as well as dyslexia, affect reading fluency.

# How to Improve Reading Fluency

We have found that the most effective and simple way to improve reading fluency is to use our reading drills for 5 minutes at least twice a week. These drills focus on increasing reading speed and accuracy in a systematic, phonetic approach.

- Daily 5 to 6-minute fluency intervention focused on phonics, sight words, and oral reading shows greater improvement than longer sessions.
- Cecil Mercer, 2010, showed significant growth in reading level and reading rate when this strategy was followed.
- The National Reading Panel, 2000, (p. 2-99) states "Systematic phonics instruction makes a bigger contribution to growth in reading skills than unsystematic or no phonics instruction."
- Research reported in the Journal of Learning Disabilities, 2003, indicates that explicit repeated practice is an effective and efficient way of achieving word reading skills in and out of connected text reading.

*Five Minutes to Better Reading Skills* addresses the four components of reading fluency:

- **Phonological Awareness**
  It incorporates every vowel and consonant combination in the English language, with lots of review built in.
- **Perceptual Awareness**
  Visual memory, visual closure, visual tracking, auditory memory, auditory-visual integration, and auditory-visual coordination skills.
- **Automaticity**
  It facilitates the ability to increase reading speed.
- **Progress Tracking**
  It has students chart their progress, so they can see their improvement.

# Benefits Beyond Fluency

### Comprehension

Fluency training inherently builds comprehension skills. Mary Leonard Palmer states, "There is a strong correlation between reading comprehension, writing, and reading fluency."

As fluency improves, students are able to hold longer pieces of text in memory, improving comprehension. To help cement this gain in place, immediately after completing a reading fluency drill, students should read from a reading selection that is suitable for their age and reading level. Their enhanced fluency carries over from the fluency drill. The student already feels successful because they have seen their improvement on their mastery charts.

After reading their story or text, I further recommend students take notes on what they have read. A great tool to use for this is the fill-in-the-blank graphic organizer forms from *The Graphic Organizer Handbook*, available from https://graphicorganizer.co. Finally, to help build long-term retention, students should answer comprehension questions from their reading selection a day or two after taking their notes.

### Visual Processing

These reading fluency drills strengthen several areas of their visual perception. In the beginning sections of each drill, the words are purposely spaced out. This is so that the student needs to pull the word together, which strengthens their visual closure skills. The drills also build visual tracking skills, by strengthening eye muscles.

### Auditory Processing

The more students practice the fluency drills, the more rapidly their auditory processing improves: auditory memory, auditory-visual integration, and auditory-visual coordination skills. These areas help retrieve, relate, and coordinate an auditory sound with a visual symbol. Strengthening these areas of auditory processing directly improves the ability to read fluently.

# Research Supports Reading Fluency

Students who read slowly typically have difficulty sounding out words, focusing, and attending to reading content. As a result, both their comprehension and writing skills are impacted.

Multiple studies by Palmer, Bashir, and Hook found a strong positive correlation between reading fluency, reading comprehension, and writing skills.

Reid Lyon, Ph.D., stated in 1997, "While the ability to read words accurately is a necessary skill in learning to read, the speed at which this is done becomes a critical factor in ensuring that children understand what they read. As one child recently remarked, 'If you don't ride a bike fast enough, you fall off.' Likewise, if the reader does not recognize words quickly enough, the meaning will be lost… If the reading of the words on the page is slow and labored, the reader simply cannot remember what he or she has read, much less relate the ideas they have read about to their own background knowledge."

A 2017 study by Taylor, Davis, and Rastle showed that learning to read by sounding out words (phonics) has a dramatic impact on both the accuracy of reading aloud and on comprehension. Researchers tested whether learning to read by sounding out words is more effective than focusing on whole-word meanings. Their results suggest that early literacy should focus on print-to-sound (phonics) rather than on teaching meaning-based strategies.

Children are more successful with decoding words when they are able to identify or recognize words quickly and nearly effortlessly. This is the concept of automaticity: the student's ability to recognize words rapidly with little attention required to the word's appearance. L. C. Ehri (1998) states that the ability to read words by sight automatically is the key to skilled reading. Fluency training is that key.

# Research Using Five Minutes to Better Reading Skills

Dr. Debra Wilson from *S'Cool Moves for Learning* conducted an independent 5-year study using *Five Minutes to Better Reading Skills*. Curriculum Based Measurement (CBM) was used to record student fluency rates.

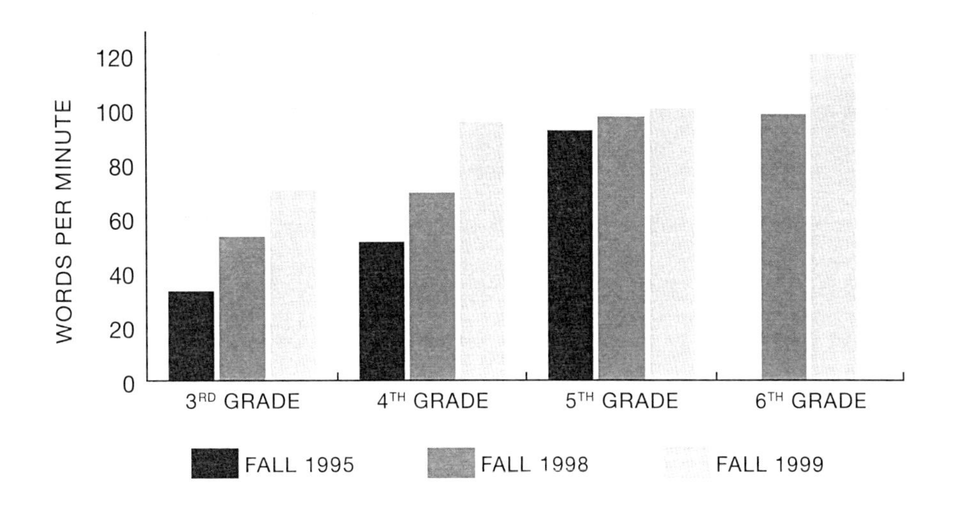


The chart below shows the results of the average increase in reading fluency for 100+ students over 15 years at Bonnie Terry's private learning center.

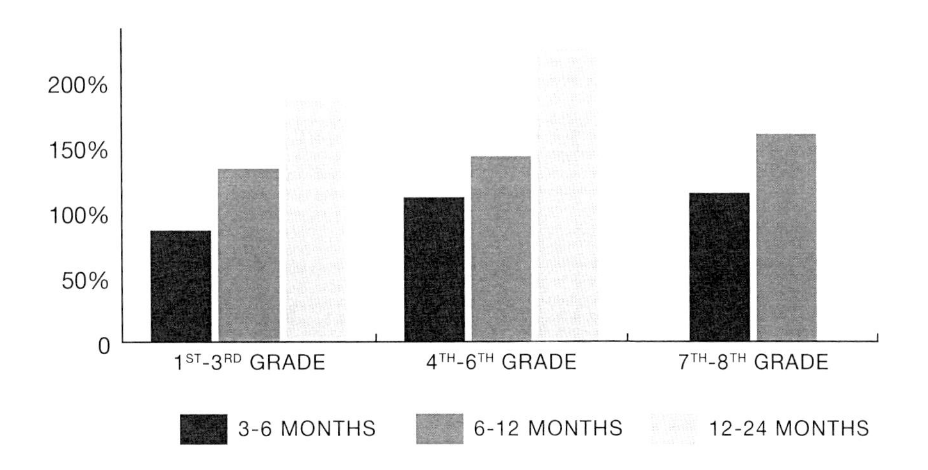


Additional studies from the University of Florida have replicated these results showing significant growth in reading level and reading rate.

Section 2:

# Directions and Tips for Mastery

# Directions

## Time Involved

This system takes 5 minutes per day. We suggest a minimum of twice a week, up to 5 times a week.

## Preparation

Students read from the student edition with instructors following along in the instructor's edition. The instructor's edition has word number counts on the right side to make it easy to keep track of the number of words read. There are no numbers on the right side of the student's drills so that the student is not distracted with the number of words they have read.

## Step 1: Pre-Read: Student Practice (2-3 min)

Have the student read the drill aloud from left to right. It is important to practice reading the drills in the same way we read books and online material.

Instructors follow along with their copy (with number counts), orally correcting any mistakes along the way. This **pre-read** helps students become familiar with the letter-sound combinations and also creates a non-stressful situation.

## Step 2: Timed Read (1 min)

Next, have the student do a one-minute timed reading of the page, keeping track of their mistakes privately and making note of any errors. An error is a **misread**, **skipped**, or **repeated** word. Do not orally correct mistakes during the timed reading. You can review any mistakes after the timed reading is completed.

If the student gets to the bottom of the page before one-minute is up, they go back to the beginning - the first line on the page - and continue reading until one-minute is up.

## Step 3: Chart Progress (1 min)

Have the student use the Daily Chart to log their total words-read-per-minute (including mistakes) on the top grid. Also chart total mistakes-per-minute in the bottom grid. This is a great way for students to be able to see their improvement: words-read-per-minute increasing and mistakes-per-minute decreasing. Use different colored pencils each day to make the chart more interesting.

*Directions continue on next page...*

## Set Passing Goals

Set a goal of no more than 4 mistakes and 5 to 25 words-per-minute improvement from their first time doing the drill. When the goal is reached, move on to the next drill. For example, if a student reads 10 words-per-minute the first time, set a goal of 15 words-per-minute before moving on to the next drill. If a student reads 45 words-per-minute the first time, set the goal of 55 to 60 words-per-minute before moving on to the next drill. If a student reads 75 words-per-minute the first time, you may set the goal of 90 to 110 words-per-minute before moving on to the next drill.

## Small Group Reading: Neural-Impress Reading Method

You may also have your whole reading group do the oral pre-read together (read the drill you are working on simultaneously as a group) before reading from your regular reading books.

This has several benefits:

- Sets up all students for success
- Reviews phonic sounds they will be encountering
- Improves fluency
- Helps readers that are not as fluent with the rhythm of reading

This method is called group neural-impress reading.

## Using the Reading Drills By Yourself

When you do not have someone to assist you with the drills, record yourself reading the drill. Then listen back and follow along with the instructor's edition, marking any mistakes you made. Then chart your progress on the daily chart.

# Tips for Mastery

1. All ages begin with Drill 1, achieve mastery, then go on to Drill 2 and so on. Each drill is built upon prior drills. If you skip one, the student will have too many new components to learn, and important sound combinations may be missed. Students may miss out on both the sounds and the knowledge of which letters make those sounds.

2. Depending on the difficulty of the drill and age of the student, set the goal between 5 to 25 more words-per-minute higher than the first timed reading. Most students will need several days per drill to achieve mastery of each drill. The "sweet spot" for meeting your target goal is to reach it over 3 to 5 days.

3. It is not possible for a student to achieve mastery in only one reading of a drill or by repeating the drill in the same day. In other words, you really need to spend 3 to 5 days per drill. If they pass on the second day, you typically haven't set your goal high enough. Use the words-per-minute read from the first timed reading as the baseline for setting the goal.

4. If your student is taking more than 5 days to reach their goal, you may need to re-evaluate the goal. It may have been set too high.

5. As students get older, it is often helpful to have them set their own goal. Just be sure they set it high enough. Sometimes kids just try to pass a goal quickly. More often than not, though, they set the goal at an appropriate level.

6. There are a few words in the reading drills that students may not be familiar with. Be sure to explain the meaning of them. For example, many students don't know what the word '*cog*' in Drill 2 is. I explain a cog is the pointy prong on the cogwheel that their bike chain goes on. Then I explain many curtain rods and blinds also have cogwheels that help you to open the curtains and blinds. Students have fewer problems reading words they understand the meaning of.

# Reading Fluency Mastery Rates

A 2nd grader with good retrieval automaticity should be able to read 80 to 100 words-per-minute. By 6th grade, they should be reading 180 words-per-minute, and by high school, they should be reading 190 to 250 words-per-minute. A 190 to 220 words-per-minute reading rate is needed for efficient reading in the college entrance SAT and ACT exams.

This mastery guide shows grade level expectations. Set your student's reading drill goal using their first timed read for each drill. If a student begins the program at a lower reading rate than their current grade level, as time goes on, their words-per-minute goal will gradually move up to meet their grade level expectation.

### Mastery Guide Reading Rates for Students

|  |  |
|---|---|
| 1st Grade *(Spring)* | 40 - 80 wpm |
| 2nd Grade *(Spring)* | 80 - 120 wpm |
| 3rd Grade *(Spring)* | 115 - 140 wpm |
| 4th Grade *(Spring)* | 140 - 170 wpm |
| 5th Grade *(Spring)* | 160 - 195 wpm |
| 6th Grade *(Spring)* | 180 - 220 wpm |

### High Risk Students

Children that schools consider to be high risk for reading failure have the following levels:

|  |  |
|---|---|
| 1st Grade *(Spring)* | 10 wpm |
| 2nd Grade *(Spring)* | 50 wpm |
| 3rd Grade *(Spring)* | 70 wpm |
| 4th Grade *(Spring)* | 80 wpm |
| 5th Grade *(Spring)* | 100 wpm |
| 6th Grade *(Spring)* | 120 wpm |

Be sure your high risk students do the reading drills 3 to 5 times a week.

Section 3:

# Daily and Mastery Charts

# Daily Chart

NAME Ron Reader

EXAMPLE PAGE

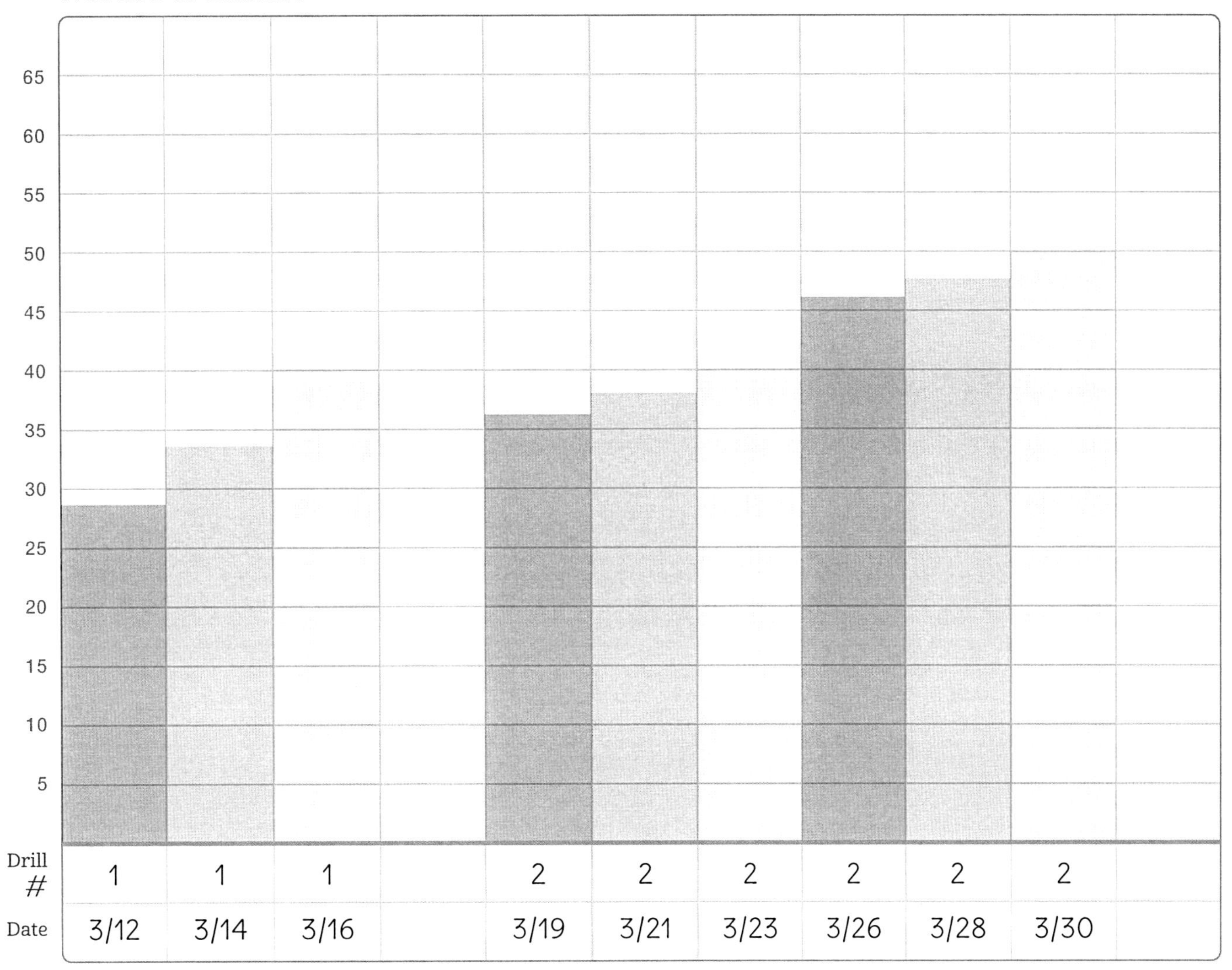


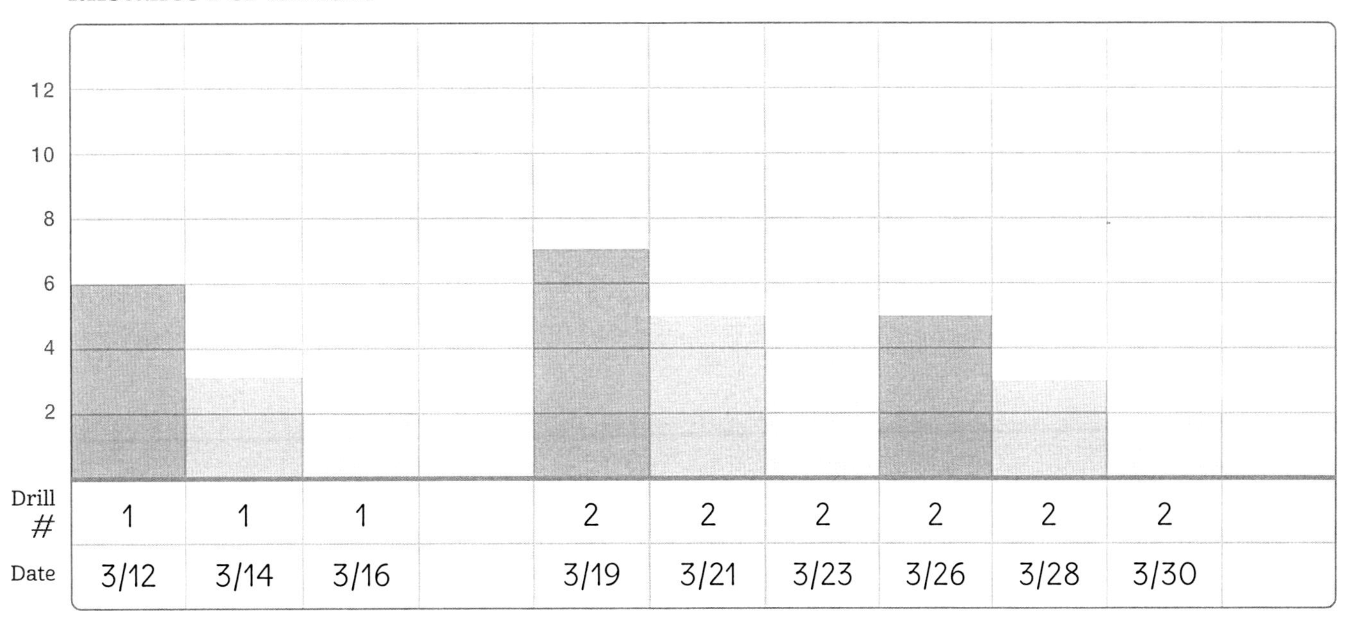

# Daily Chart

NAME

Words Per Minute

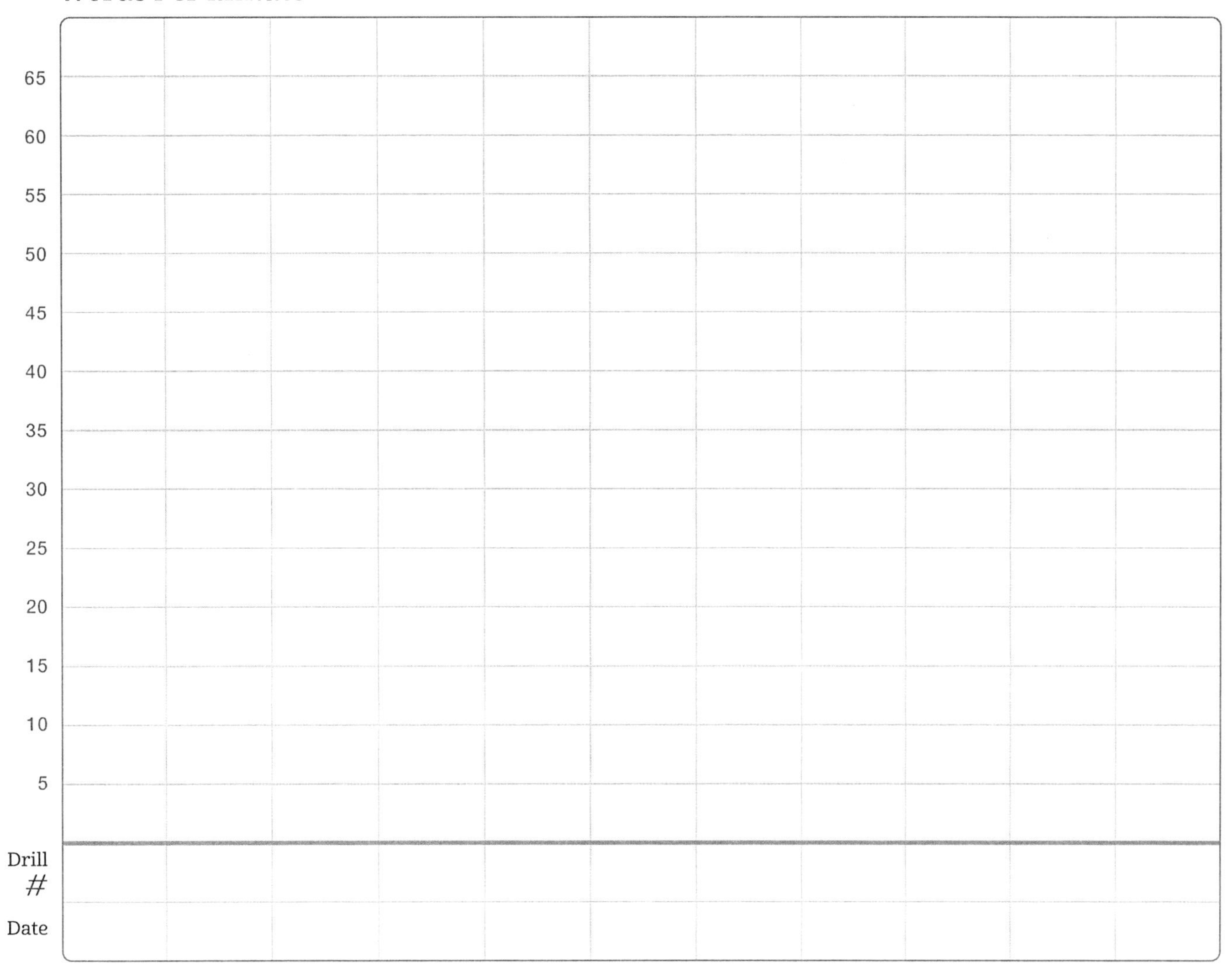


Mistakes Per Minute

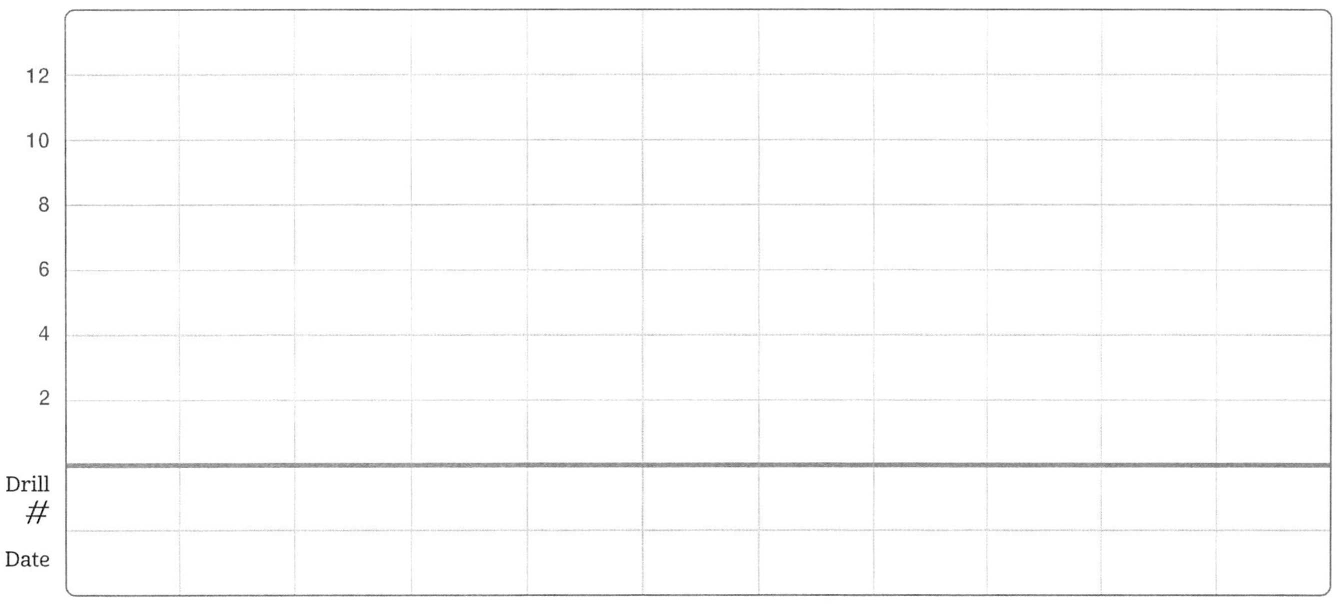

# Daily Chart

NAME

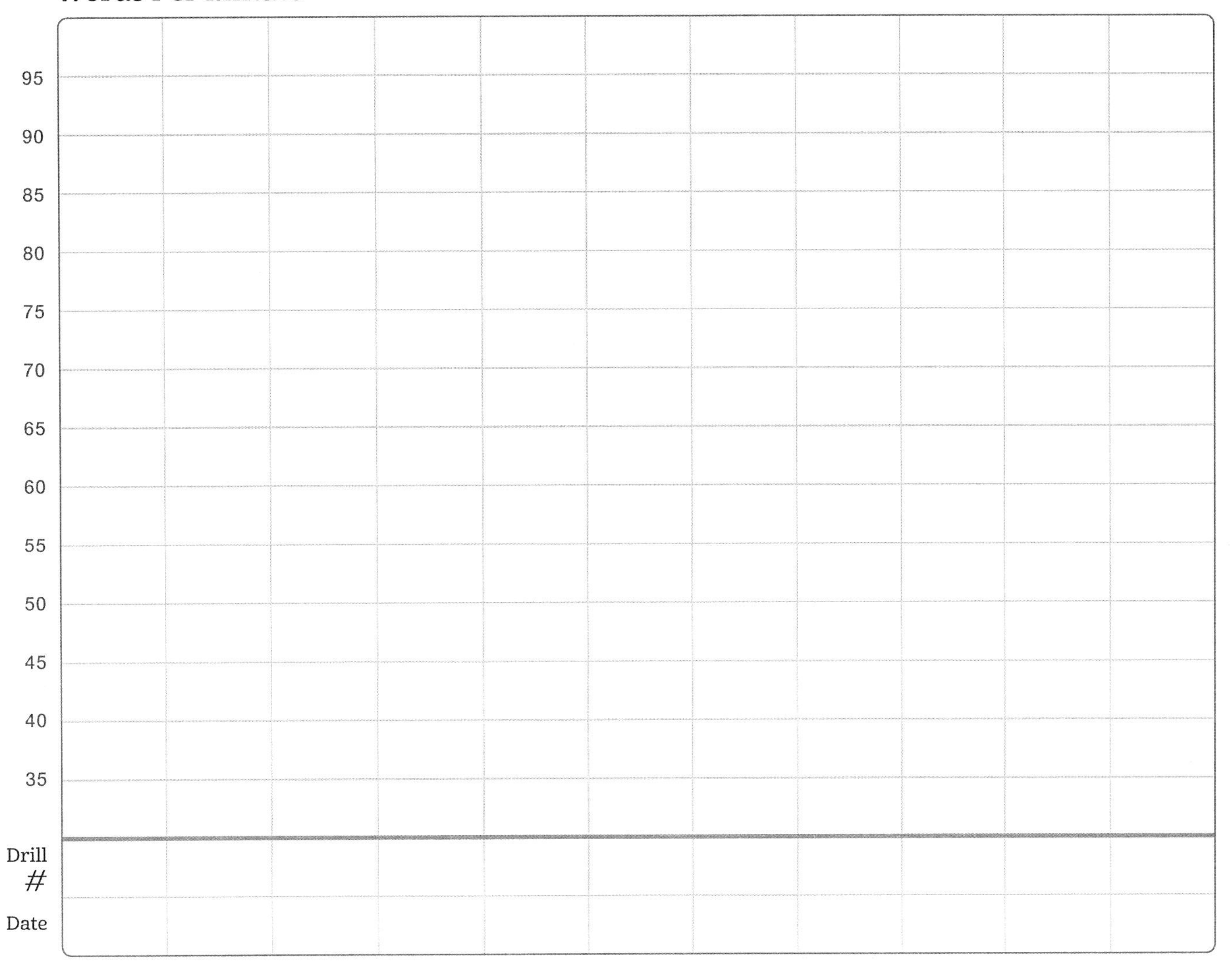


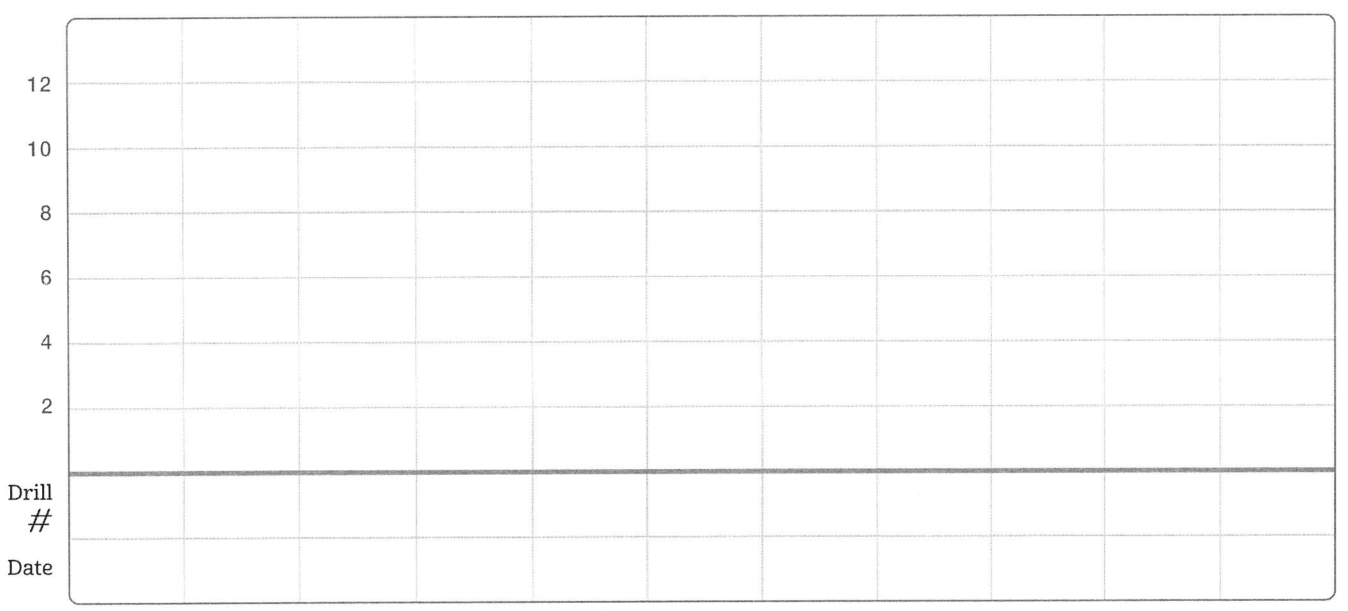

# Daily Chart

NAME

Words Per Minute

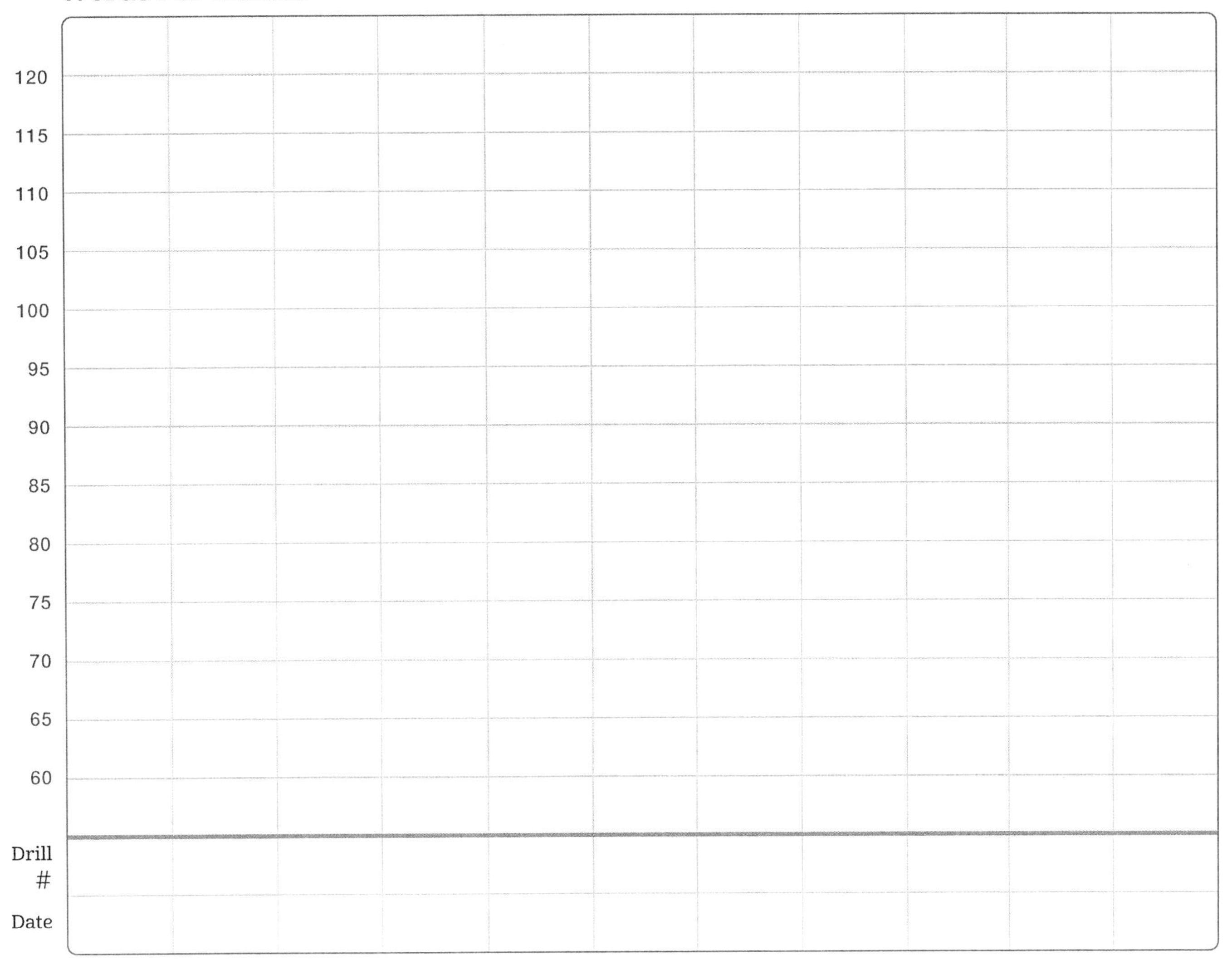


Mistakes Per Minute

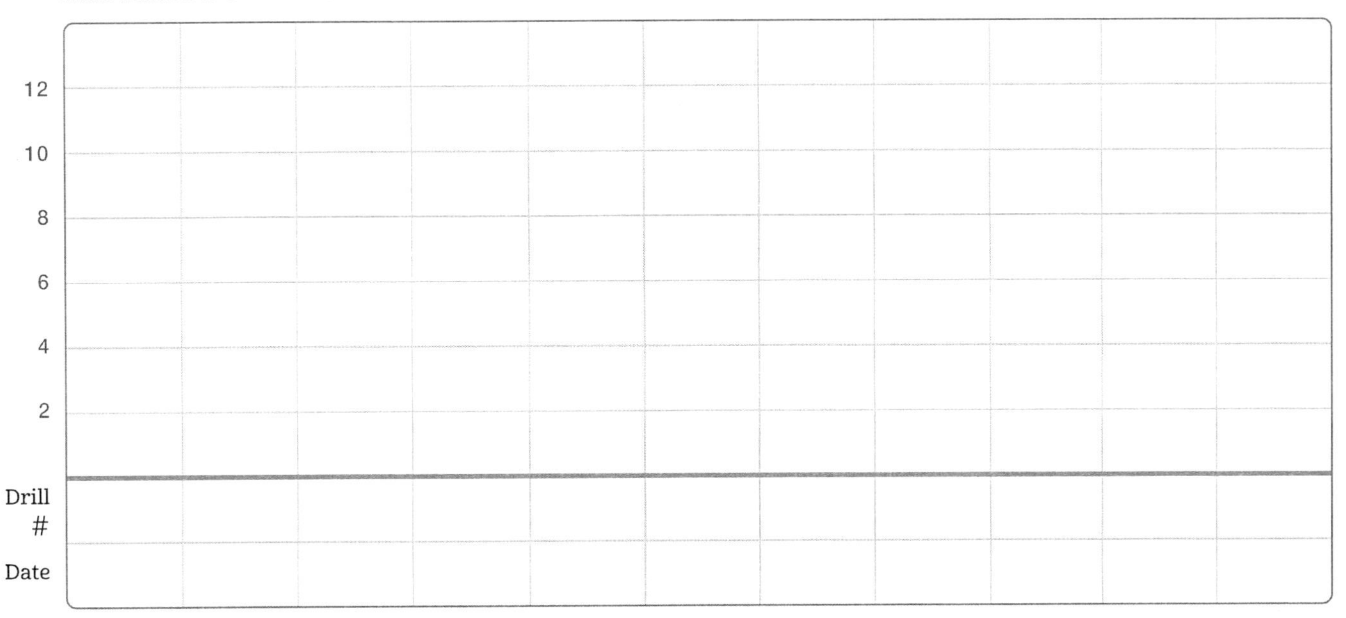

# Daily Chart

NAME

Words Per Minute

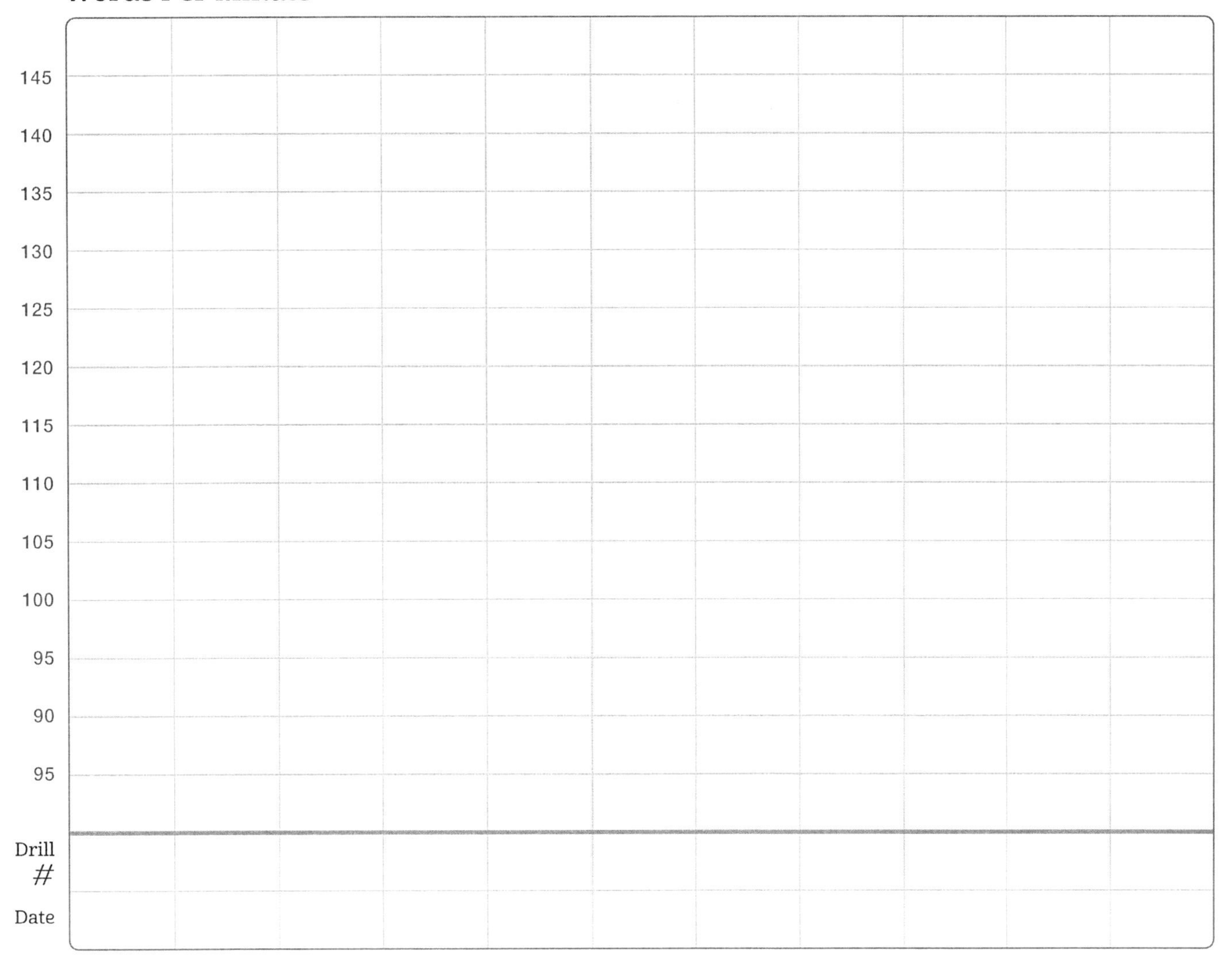


Mistakes Per Minute

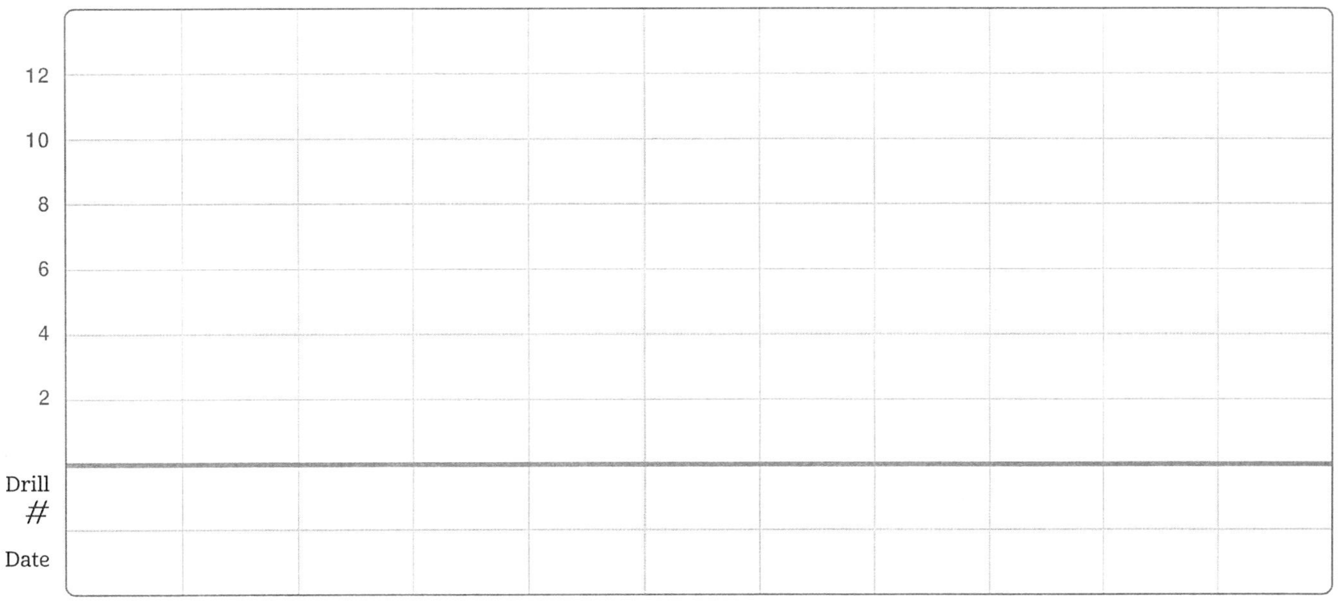

# Daily Chart

NAME

Words Per Minute

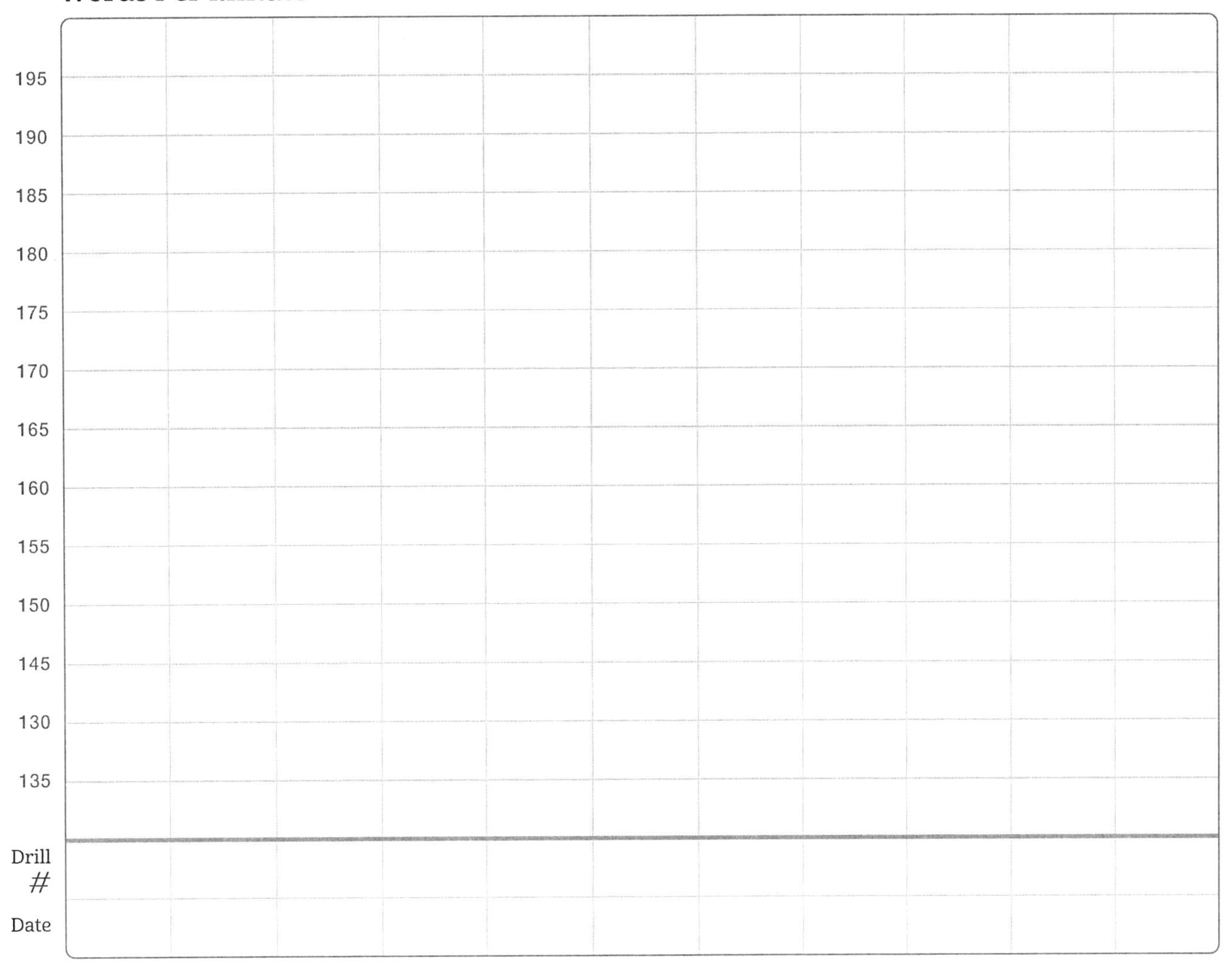


Mistakes Per Minute

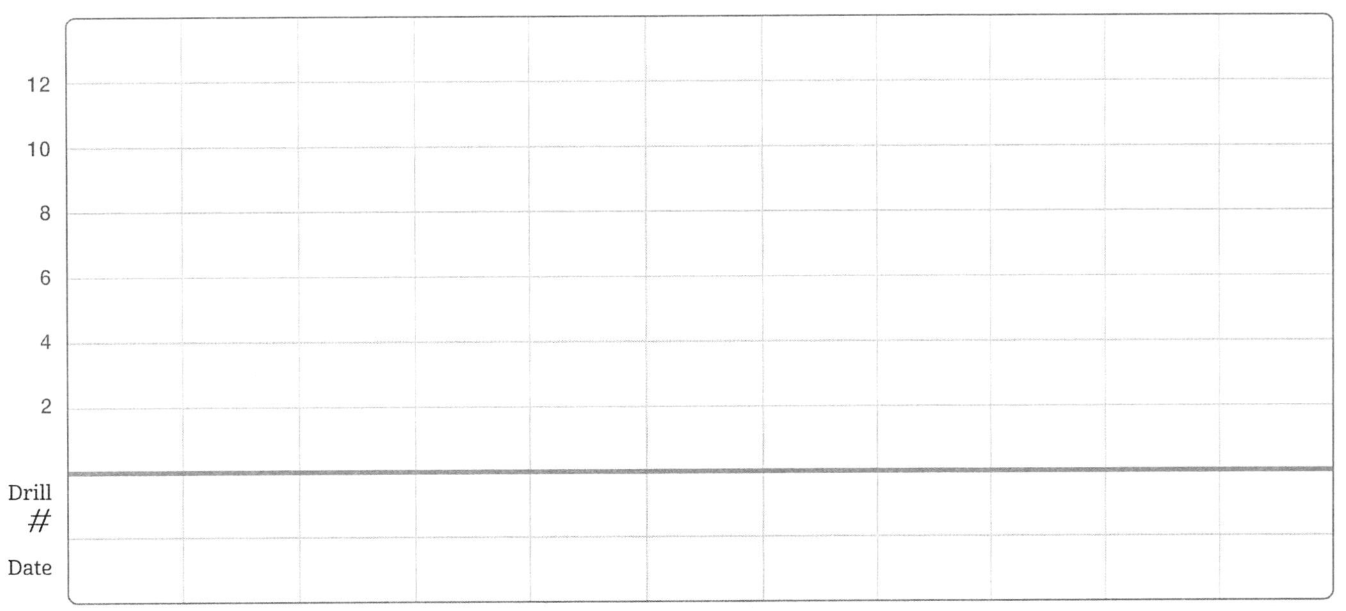

# Daily Chart

NAME

## Words Per Minute

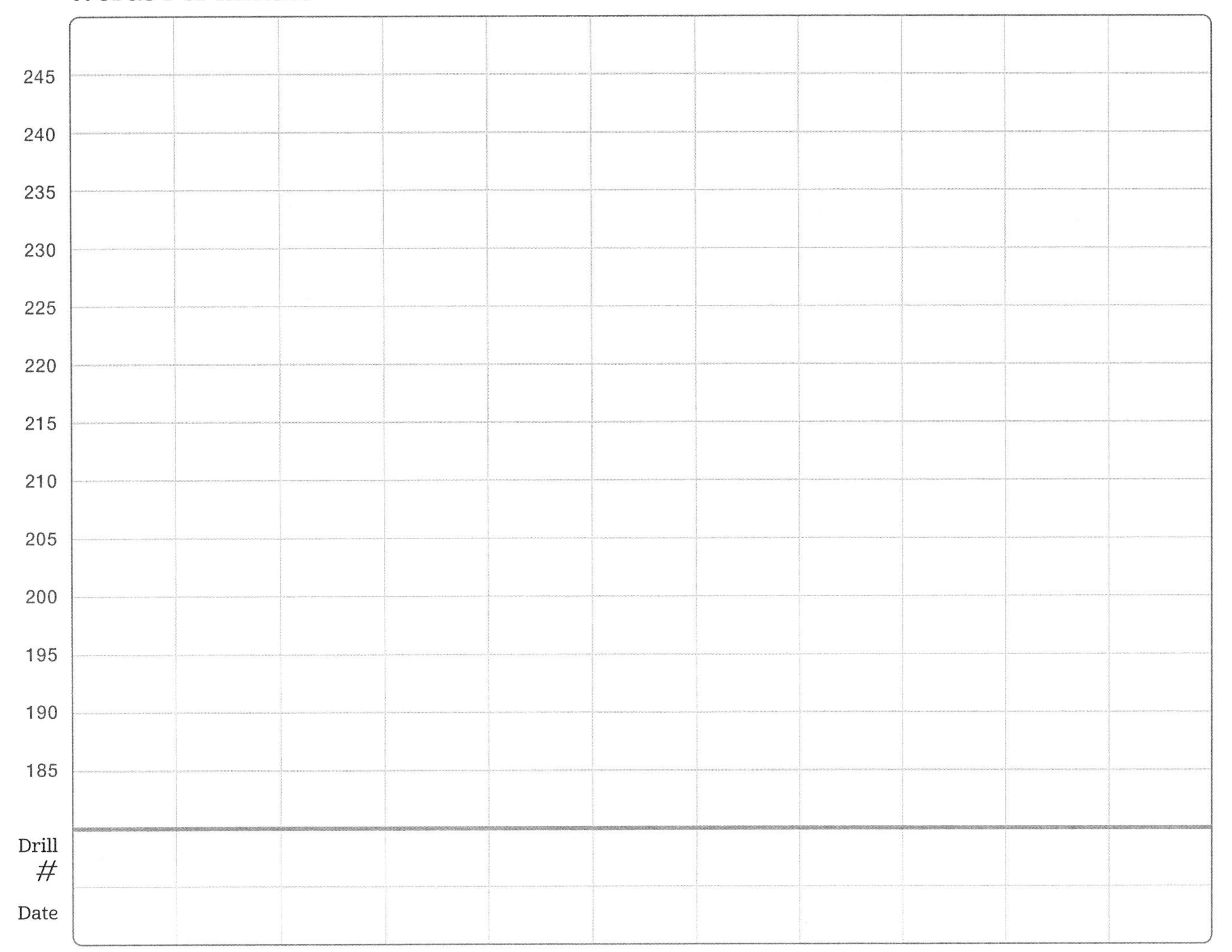


## Mistakes Per Minute

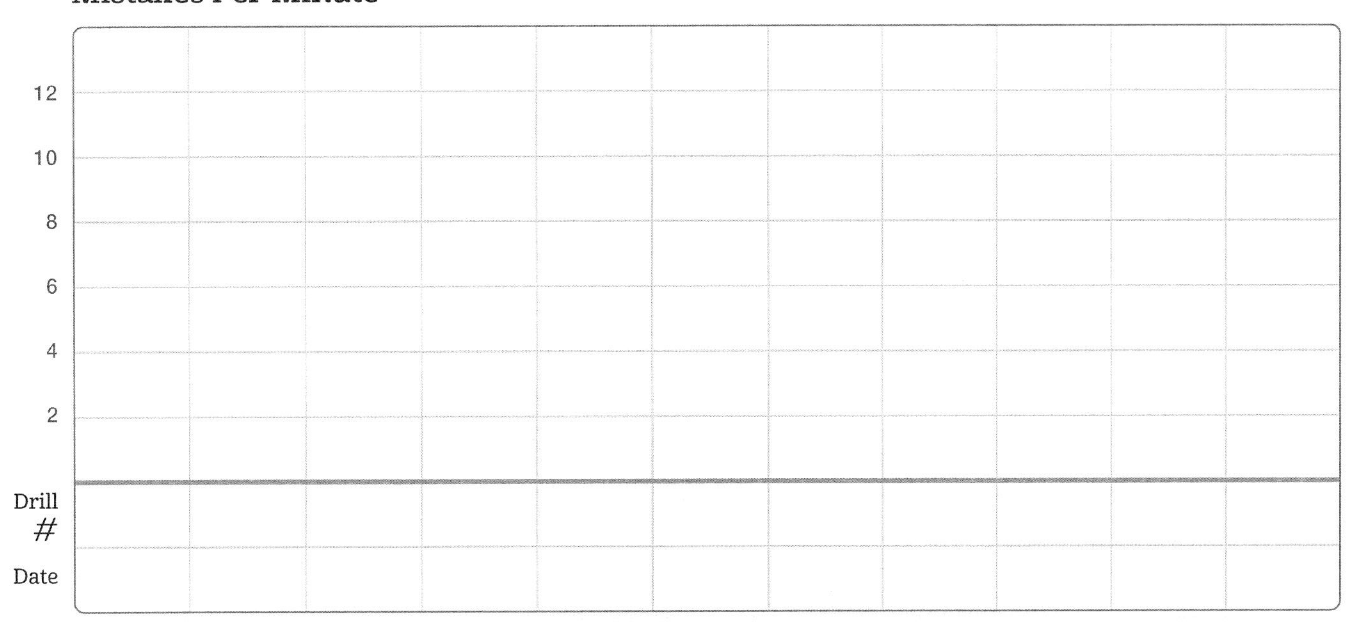

# Mastery Chart

NAME

| DRILL | LESSON | DATE STARTED | DATE MASTERED |
|---|---|---|---|
| Drill 1 | *ă* | | |
| Drill 2 | *ŏ* | | |
| Drill 3 | *Review: ă, ŏ* | | |
| Drill 4 | *ĭ* | | |
| Drill 5 | *Review: ă, ŏ, ĭ* | | |
| Drill 6 | *ŭ* | | |
| Drill 7 | *Review: ă, ŏ, ĭ, ŭ* | | |
| Drill 8 | *ēe̸, ēe̸+r (deer), ēe̸+l (feel)* | | |
| Drill 9 | *sh* | | |
| Drill 10 | *o͝o (book), o͝o+l (wool)* | | |
| Drill 11 | *o͞o (boot), ôo+r (poor), o͞o+l (tool)* | | |
| Drill 12 | *ch, tch* | | |
| Drill 13 | *Review: ă, ŏ, ĭ, ŭ, ēe̸, ēe̸+r, ēe̸+l, o͞o, o͝o, ôo+r, o͞o+l, sh, ch, tch* | | |
| Drill 14 | *är (car)* | | |
| Drill 15 | *āy̸ (pay), āi̸ (rain), āi̸+l (nail)* | | |
| Drill 16 | *ôr (for)* | | |
| Drill 17 | *ōld* | | |
| Drill 18 | *ĕ* | | |
| Drill 19 | *Review: är, āy̸, āi̸, āi̸+l, ôr, ōld, ĕ* | | |
| Drill 20 | *ā, ī, ō, ū (silent e̸)* | | |
| Drill 21 | *ōa̸, ōa̸+l (coal)* | | |
| Drill 22 | *ōw̸ (low)* | | |
| Drill 23 | *ou (out), ow (how)* | | |

# Mastery Chart

NAME

| DRILL | LESSON | DATE STARTED | DATE MASTERED |
|---|---|---|---|
| Drill 24 | *Review: ā, ī, ō, ū (silent e̸), ōa̸, ou, ōw̸, ow* | | |
| Drill 25 | *th, wh* | | |
| Drill 26 | *ng, nk* | | |
| Drill 27 | *Review: th, wh, ng, nk* | | |
| Drill 28 | *er (ur – term), ir (ur – fir), ur (ur – turf)* | | |
| Drill 29 | *au (ô – cause), aw (ô – paw)* | | |
| Drill 30 | *ea (ir – ear), ea (ĕ – head), ea (ēa̸ – team), ea (ur – earn), ea (er – wear)* | | |
| Drill 31 | *Review: er (ur), ir (ur), ur, ŏo, au (ô), aw (ô), ea (ir – ear), ea (e – head), ea (ēa̸ – team), ea (ur – earn), ea (er – wear)* | | |
| Drill 32 | *ew (ōō – crew), ue (ōō – blue), y ( ī – fly)* | | |
| Drill 33 | *oy (ōi – joy), oi (ōi – join), oi+l (ōi+l – oil)* | | |
| Drill 34 | *al (ô), alk (ô), eigh (ā)* | | |
| Drill 35 | *Review: ew (ōō), ue (ōō), y (ī), oy (ōi), ōi, al (ô), alk (ô), eigh (ā)* | | |
| Drill 36 | *c and g followed by e, i, or y; dge* | | |
| Drill 37 | *Silent Letters: ph (f), k̸n, c̸k, gh̸ (f), gh̸, gh̸t* | | |
| Drill 38 | *Review: c and g followed by e, i, or y; dge; ph (f), k̸n, c̸k, gh̸ (f), gh̸, gh̸t* | | |
| Drill 39 | *Two-Syllable Words – Words that end with consonant + y (ē) or y (ē) by itself* | | |
| | | | |

# Mastery Chart

NAME

| DRILL | LESSON | DATE STARTED | DATE MASTERED |
|---|---|---|---|
| Drill 40 | *Two-Syllable Words: Words that end with 'le' (ble, cle, dle, ple, tle, etc.)* | | |
| Drill 41 | *Review: Words that end with 'le', consonant + y (ē) or y (ē) by itself* | | |
| **Advanced Drills** | | | |
| Drill 42 | *Suffixes: ed, en, es, ing* | | |
| Drill 43 | *Suffixes: dom, ful, less, ness, sion, tion* | | |
| Drill 44 | *Suffixes: acy, ant, ary, ity, ive, tial* | | |
| Drill 45 | *Review: acy, ary, ed, en, es, dom, ful, less, ing, ity, ive, ness, ion, tial, tion* | | |
| Drill 46 | *Prefixes: de, dis, ex, mis, non, pre, re, un* | | |
| Drill 47 | *Prefixes: anti, auto, bi, dis, in, out, sub, tri* | | |
| Drill 48 | *Prefixes: ex, inter, im, mid, post, pro, tele, trans, super* | | |
| Drill 49 | *Review: anti, auto, bi, de, dis, ex, im, inter, mid, mis, non, out, post, pre, pro, re, sub, super, tele, trans, un* | | |
| Drill 50 | *Multi-Syllable Words: Prefixes and Suffixes* | | |
| Drill 51 | *More Multi-Syllable Words: Prefixes and Suffixes* | | |
| Drill 52 | *Final Review: Prefixes and Suffixes* | | |

# Section 4:
# **Reading Drills**

# Drill 1

ă

| | | | | | | |
|---|---|---|---|---|---|---|
| sat | mat | rat | bat | cat | fat | |
| cap | sap | map | tap | lap | rap | |
| am | ram | Sam | ham | dam | jam | 18 |
| rag | bag | tag | wag | hag | lag | |
| can | man | ran | tan | fan | pan | |
| sad | mad | had | lad | pad | dad | 36 |

| | | | | | | |
|---|---|---|---|---|---|---|
| sat | sap | Sam | sad | cab | cat | |
| lad | lap | fan | fat | bat | ban | |
| mat | mad | man | map | hat | ham | 54 |
| tan | tap | tag | tax | cap | can | |
| rag | ran | rat | rap | bad | bag | 66 |

| | | | | | | |
|---|---|---|---|---|---|---|
| ban | pat | tan | fat | man | sat | |
| map | can | mad | cat | man | cab | |
| rag | cat | lap | ham | bat | tap | |
| jam | fan | dam | had | tag | rap | 90 |

| | | | | | | | |
|---|---|---|---|---|---|---|---|
| sat | cap | rag | can | sad | mat | sap | |
| ram | bag | man | mad | rat | map | Sam | 104 |
| tag | ran | had | bat | tap | ham | wag | |
| tan | ran | cat | lap | dam | hag | fan | |
| pad | fat | rap | jam | lag | pan | dad | 125 |

# Drill 2

ŏ

---

| | | | | | |
|---|---|---|---|---|---|
| hot | pot | not | rot | got | |
| sob | bob | rob | job | mob | |
| hop | mop | lop | pop | top | 15 |
| cog | bog | jog | fog | hog | |
| sod | cod | pod | nod | rod | 25 |

| | | | | |
|---|---|---|---|---|
| hop | hot | hob | hog | |
| pod | pot | pop | mop | |
| cob | cot | cod | cog | 37 |
| Tom | top | Bob | tot | |
| rot | rob | rob | rod | |
| mop | mod | mop | mob | |
| sob | sod | sob | sop | 53 |

| | | | | | |
|---|---|---|---|---|---|
| hot | lop | pot | top | not | |
| rob | hop | rod | hog | rot | |
| got | Tom | nod | pop | sob | 68 |

| | | | | | | | | |
|---|---|---|---|---|---|---|---|---|
| dot | mop | Tom | jog | pop | hot | cog | cob | |
| log | pop | Bob | got | sod | hog | pot | lot | |
| rot | fog | log | pod | sob | rob | not | pop | 92 |

# Drill 3

REVIEW

ă ŏ

| | | | | | | |
|---|---|---|---|---|---|---|
| sat | bag | ram | cap | lad | tan | |
| not | hog | sod | top | mob | got | |
| tag | ham | ran | rod | fog | mop | 18 |
| lap | man | hat | rob | dot | log | |

| | | | | | | |
|---|---|---|---|---|---|---|
| cat | cot | hat | hot | pat | pot | |
| hob | had | rot | rat | map | mop | |
| hat | hog | sop | sad | top | tap | |
| cob | cab | pad | pod | Nat | not | 48 |

| | | | | | | |
|---|---|---|---|---|---|---|
| pot | cat | log | bag | pod | lad | |
| map | mop | cob | cap | tan | ton | |
| hot | jot | fat | fog | nag | lad | |
| rob | tab | sat | pod | fan | lap | |
| bob | rat | sad | cog | lot | pop | 78 |

| | | | | | | | | |
|---|---|---|---|---|---|---|---|---|
| mat | fat | job | lot | tap | mat | pat | pot | |
| rod | tab | sob | hat | fan | hot | job | fat | |
| cap | rob | wag | got | map | ran | nap | cab | |
| pat | had | jam | rob | lab | tot | not | sag | 110 |

# Drill 4

*ĭ*

---

| | | | | | |
|---|---|---|---|---|---|
| kit | sit | bit | fit | hit | |
| dim | him | rim | Jim | Tim | |
| lip | dip | hip | sip | rip | |
| win | fin | bin | sin | tin | 20 |

| | | | | | |
|---|---|---|---|---|---|
| fig | dig | big | pig | rig | |
| hid | did | kid | bid | mid | |
| rib | fib | bib | fib | rib | |
| mix | fix | six | mix | fix | 40 |

| | | | | |
|---|---|---|---|---|
| hit | him | hid | hip | |
| sin | six | Sid | sit | |
| rib | rid | rim | rig | |
| tin | tip | Tim | tin | |
| lip | lid | lit | lip | |
| pig | pit | pin | pig | 64 |

| | | | | | | |
|---|---|---|---|---|---|---|
| dim | hit | fit | kit | sit | rip | |
| sip | sin | win | rip | hip | tin | |
| rig | hid | hit | rim | hip | rid | |
| mid | bin | dig | dip | pit | lip | |
| did | fin | fib | mix | rib | big | 94 |

# Drill 5

REVIEW

*ă ŏ ĭ*

---

| | | | | | | |
|---|---|---|---|---|---|---|
| mat | cab | rag | cap | can | sad | |
| hop | sob | not | cog | sod | pot | |
| sip | him | win | fig | hid | sit | |
| Bob | sap | man | fit | rim | mob | 24 |

| | | | | | | |
|---|---|---|---|---|---|---|
| hat | hot | hit | pit | pot | pat | |
| tap | top | tip | hid | hod | had | |
| big | bag | bog | lip | lop | lap | |
| hot | hit | hat | tap | tip | top | 48 |

| | | | | | | |
|---|---|---|---|---|---|---|
| cab | sat | bit | dot | cap | sip | |
| rag | rim | rib | sad | sob | sip | |
| hot | dim | fog | mat | sip | lag | 66 |
| bog | pot | nip | jig | dim | hot | |
| bag | hip | sat | fan | jig | did | |
| fix | rob | wag | dip | got | map | 84 |

| | | | | | | | | |
|---|---|---|---|---|---|---|---|---|
| pan | sod | lot | pit | jog | six | rip | ram | |
| Jim | bog | cot | Sam | rim | bog | tan | mob | |
| rat | hog | dot | bog | pop | Dan | kid | rap | |
| sad | big | wag | fin | did | nap | top | tag | 116 |

# Drill 6

*ŭ*

---

| | | | | | | |
|---|---|---|---|---|---|---|
| nut | hut | cut | gut | but | jut | |
| gun | sun | run | fun | nun | bun | |
| up | pup | up | cup | pup | cup | |
| dug | rug | mug | pug | jug | bug | 24 |
| hub | tub | rub | hub | rub | tub | |
| dud | bud | mud | cud | mud | bud | |
| sum | gum | rum | sum | hum | gum | 42 |

| | | | | |
|---|---|---|---|---|
| hub | hug | hum | hut | |
| rub | run | rut | run | |
| bud | bug | bun | but | 54 |
| pup | sum | sun | cup | |
| cut | cup | cud | cup | |
| gun | gut | gun | gum | 66 |

| | | | | | | |
|---|---|---|---|---|---|---|
| bud | hub | rug | but | fun | cup | |
| run | bus | cut | hut | nut | pup | |
| sun | rug | but | cup | hum | nun | |
| mud | hum | rub | run | pup | mug | |
| sup | tub | mug | tub | pug | cud | 96 |

| | | | | | | | | | |
|---|---|---|---|---|---|---|---|---|---|
| hut | mud | hug | rub | bus | sub | rug | jug | run | |
| but | dug | jut | tug | gun | rum | hub | nut | tub | |
| up | gun | cut | sun | gum | tub | mud | hum | fun | |
| gut | hut | jut | pup | bug | bun | sum | cup | hut | 132 |

# Drill 7

REVIEW

*ă ŏ ĭ ŭ*

---

| | | | | | | |
|---|---|---|---|---|---|---|
| pad | mad | lag | fat | rap | pan | |
| rib | fib | pig | lid | him | bit | |
| rip | sat | hit | fad | hip | cap | |
| pan | sob | pop | Tom | hog | hop | |
| cup | nut | fun | hub | rug | bud | 30 |

| | | | | | | |
|---|---|---|---|---|---|---|
| hub | hug | hum | hut | hat | hot | |
| big | bag | bog | bug | cat | cot | |
| hit | hot | hut | hat | sip | sap | |
| rum | rim | ram | jug | jog | jig | |
| bat | but | bit | him | ham | hum | 60 |

| | | | | | |
|---|---|---|---|---|---|
| hit | cup | nut | cob | Sam | |
| got | dad | nap | gum | mud | |
| fib | sum | wax | box | cut | 75 |
| sin | tug | rat | tag | run | |
| sip | lot | sod | ox | but | |
| gum | pit | cab | pop | Tim | 90 |

| | | | | | | | | |
|---|---|---|---|---|---|---|---|---|
| fib | hag | tab | bun | cot | cut | pit | six | |
| top | tan | mob | tub | hid | pig | rip | dad | |
| dot | wax | him | but | pat | Tom | hip | dad | |
| mix | man | dip | bob | pup | dot | hip | sap | |
| bag | rod | Jim | pop | cut | pod | got | bug | 130 |

# Drill 8

***ēe̸*** ***ēe̸+r*** *(deer)* ***ēe̸+l*** *(feel)*

---

| | | | | | | |
|---|---|---|---|---|---|---|
| d ee d | s ee d | w ee d | n ee d | s ee d | f ee d | |
| b ee r | d ee r | j ee r | l ee r | p ee r | d ee r | |
| r ee l | k ee l | p ee l | h ee l | f ee l | p ee l | |
| s ee k | p ee k | w ee k | m ee t | b ee t | m ee t | |
| p ee p | k ee p | d ee p | d ee m | t ee m | s ee m | 30 |

| | | | | | |
|---|---|---|---|---|---|
| r ee d | r ee k | r ee l | r ee d | r ee f | |
| d ee r | d ee p | d ee m | d ee p | d ee d | |
| p ee k | p ee p | p ee l | p ee r | p ee k | 45 |
| s ee d | s ee | s ee n | s ee k | s ee m | |
| w ee | w ee d | w ee p | w ee k | w ee d | |
| k ee l | k ee p | k ee n | k ee p | k ee n | 60 |

| | | | | | | |
|---|---|---|---|---|---|---|
| d ee r | s ee | d ee p | d ee d | r ee d | p ee r | |
| b ee | p ee l | f ee | s ee | r ee k | r ee f | |
| p ee k | b ee r | f ee t | w ee d | l ee | s ee k | |
| m ee t | k ee l | l ee k | k ee n | b ee t | m ee k | |
| f ee l | l ee r | n ee d | w ee d | w ee k | k ee p | 90 |

| | | | | | | | |
|---|---|---|---|---|---|---|---|
| deep | weep | feed | peep | reel | beef | seep | |
| seem | peel | heel | beet | keen | reed | deep | |
| feet | week | leer | beet | heed | keep | need | |
| jeer | see | teem | deed | keep | deep | seem | 118 |

# Drill 9

*sh*

---

| | | | | | |
|---|---|---|---|---|---|
| c a sh | d a sh | g a sh | l a sh | b a sh | |
| m a sh | r a sh | d a sh | s a sh | g a sh | |
| d i sh | w i sh | f i sh | d i sh | w i sh | |
| g u sh | m u sh | h u sh | r u sh | l u sh | 20 |

| | | | | | |
|---|---|---|---|---|---|
| sh ee p | sh ee r | sh ee n | sh ee t | sh ee p | |
| sh o d | sh o p | sh o d | sh o p | sh o t | |
| sh i p | sh u n | sh i n | sh u t | sh i m | 35 |

| | | | | |
|---|---|---|---|---|
| sh ee r | d a sh | sh i p | m a sh | |
| sh o p | d i sh | sh ee t | g u sh | |
| c a sh | sh i n | r u sh | r a sh | |
| sh o t | f i sh | m u sh | g a sh | 51 |
| h u sh | sh o p | w i sh | sh u t | |
| s a sh | sh ee n | l a sh | sh u t | |
| sh a m | l a sh | sh ee p | c a sh | 63 |

| | | | | | | |
|---|---|---|---|---|---|---|
| hush | sheep | shod | cash | fish | shun | |
| sheen | dash | dish | shin | ship | mush | |
| sheep | lash | gash | rush | shop | sham | |
| mash | shot | gush | wish | shut | sheet | 87 |

# Drill 10

**ŏŏ** *(book)* **ŏŏ+l** *(wool)*

---

| | | | | | |
|---|---|---|---|---|---|
| w oo l | s oo t | sh oo k | l oo k | h oo d | |
| cr oo k | f oo t | c oo k | b oo k | n oo k | |
| g oo d | b oo k | l oo k | h oo d | t oo k | |
| h oo f | h oo d | w oo f | s oo t | h oo d | 20 |

| | | | | | |
|---|---|---|---|---|---|
| b oo k | t oo k | sh oo k | f oo t | s oo t | |
| n oo k | c r oo k | c oo k | s oo t | h oo d | |
| g oo d | w oo l | h oo d | sh oo k | l oo k | |
| c r oo k | h oo d | g oo d | c oo k | sh oo k | 40 |

| | | | | | |
|---|---|---|---|---|---|
| b oo k | l oo k | g oo d | sh oo k | w oo l | |
| n oo k | f oo t | g oo d | h oo d | t oo k | |
| s oo t | c oo k | t oo k | b oo k | n oo k | |
| g oo d | w oo l | l oo k | h oo d | t oo k | 60 |

| | | | | | | |
|---|---|---|---|---|---|---|
| book | took | wool | hood | nook | shook | |
| crook | good | hood | soot | look | took | |
| cook | foot | look | shook | nook | book | |
| shook | wool | good | took | cook | hood | 84 |

# Drill 11

**o͞o** *(boot)* **ôo+r** *(poor)* **o͞o+l** *(tool)*

---

| | | | | | |
|---|---|---|---|---|---|
| b oo t | h oo t | r oo t | sh oo t | t oo t | |
| b oo n | n oo n | s oo n | t oo n | m oo n | |
| c oo l | t oo l | p oo l | f oo l | st oo l | |
| r oo m | l oo m | b oo m | d oo m | bl oo m | 20 |
| f oo d | m oo d | l oo p | m oo d | h oo t | |
| t oo t | r oo f | g oo f | r oo f | r oo t | |
| h oo p | l oo p | fl oo r | p oo r | d oo r | 35 |

| | | | | |
|---|---|---|---|---|
| r oo t | r oo f | r oo m | r oo t | |
| b oo t | b oo m | b oo t | b oo n | |
| h oo t | h oo p | d oo r | h oo p | |
| m oo t | m oo d | m oo n | m oo d | 51 |

| | | | | | |
|---|---|---|---|---|---|
| f oo d | r oo m | b oo t | m oo n | c oo l | |
| r oo m | h oo p | h oo t | f oo l | st oo l | |
| t oo t | l oo p | r oo t | s oo n | l oo m | 66 |
| s oo n | st oo l | d oo m | r oo t | fl oo r | |
| r oo f | sh oo t | n oo n | b oo m | t oo t | |
| p oo r | d oo r | c oo l | d oo m | b oo t | 81 |

| | | | | | | | |
|---|---|---|---|---|---|---|---|
| pool | loot | food | root | door | poor | noon | |
| boot | loom | soon | toot | poor | shoot | roof | |
| stool | noon | loop | food | hoot | room | doom | |
| boot | soon | tool | shoot | cool | boon | fool | 109 |

# Drill 12

*ch tch*

---

ch a p ch a t ch a ff ch a p ch o p
ch i n ch i ll ch i p ch i ll b ee ch
ch ee k ch ee p ch ee r ch ee k ch i n
ch o p ch u m b ee ch r i ch s u ch 20

w i tch p i tch h i tch i tch d i tch
h a tch p a tch c a tch m a tch l a tch
m u ch b ee ch r i ch s u ch m u ch 35

r i ch ch a p ch i n d i tch ch a t
p i tch ch i p c a tch p i tch ch ee k
ch a ff h i tch n o tch m a tch p i tch
ch i ll i tch m a tch ch u m ch o p 55
p a tch ch o p b ee ch ch a ff ch u m
l a tch ch a t d i tch n o tch b a tch
ch i ll b ee ch r i ch h a tch c a tch 70

chin rich chap notch chill cheek
latch chop chin chum chip catch
batch chin chaff cheer hitch chop
chat itch ditch chum chum pitch
patch chip chaff notch chap rich 100

# Drill 13

REVIEW

*ă ŏ ĭ ŭ ēe̸ ēe̸+r ēe̸+l*

*o͞o o͝o ôo+r o͞o+l sh ch tch*

---

| d i sh | s a sh | sh o d | c a sh | sh o p | sh u t | |
|---|---|---|---|---|---|---|
| g u sh | sh ee p | sh o t | d a sh | m ee t | s ee | |
| f ee t | b oo t | sh oo t | sh ee t | s ee n | s oo n | |
| p oo r | p ee r | f oo l | f ee l | sh ee t | sh oo t | |
| m oo n | n oo n | h u sh | f ee d | f ee t | d ee d | 30 |

| h i tch | ch o p | c a tch | r i ch | ch u m | ch a t | |
|---|---|---|---|---|---|---|
| ch i p | sh o p | ch o p | c a sh | sh i p | c a tch | |
| d i tch | sh i n | d i sh | m u ch | m u sh | ch i n | |
| c a sh | sh u t | sh o t | sh o d | ch i ll | s u ch | |
| n o tch | ch i n | st oo l | r oo f | p oo l | b oo m | 60 |

| h oo p | l a tch | sh ee p | b oo t | ch i ll | d ee m | |
|---|---|---|---|---|---|---|
| b ee t | sh i p | l ee k | sh i p | t ee n | h oo f | |
| h i tch | p o ll | l oo p | r oo f | m a sh | m u sh | |
| sh o p | r ee d | m oo d | m oo n | m a tch | d i sh | 84 |

| woof | chin | doom | gush | feet | peep | |
|---|---|---|---|---|---|---|
| itch | sheet | jeer | cheer | cash | loon | |
| tool | shin | noon | rash | keen | rich | 102 |
| food | shot | chap | noon | fish | catch | |
| hoot | pitch | deep | mush | patch | feed | |
| keen | root | gash | deed | sheer | catch | 120 |

# Drill 14

**är** *(car)*

---

| | | | | | |
|---|---|---|---|---|---|
| t ar | j ar | c ar | f ar | b ar | |
| c ar | s t ar | s c ar | m ar | f ar | |
| c ar t | d ar t | m ar t | p ar t | d ar t | |
| y ar d | h ar d | l ar d | c ar d | h ar d | |
| ar k | l ar k | sh ar k | p ar k | d ar k | 25 |

| | | | | | |
|---|---|---|---|---|---|
| ar ch | ar t | ar m | ar k | ar m | |
| h ar d | h ar p | h ar t | sh ar p | h ar d | |
| b ar n | b ar k | b ar | b ar k | b ar n | 40 |
| c ar | C ar l | c ar d | c ar | c ar t | |
| d ar t | d ar n | d ar t | d ar k | d ar n | |
| m ar | m ar ch | m ar sh | m ar t | m ar k | 55 |

| | | | | | |
|---|---|---|---|---|---|
| b ar | y ar n | ar m | c ar d | y ar n | |
| y ar d | l ar k | d ar t | b ar n | ar k | |
| s c ar | s t ar | f ar m | p ar k | ch ar m | |
| h ar p | c ar d | sh ar k | p ar t | c ar t | |
| b ar b | m ar sh | g ar b | t ar | sh ar p | 80 |

| | | | | | | | |
|---|---|---|---|---|---|---|---|
| chart | farm | hark | mark | lard | mark | march | |
| part | car | dark | hard | star | park | charm | |
| far | bark | card | dark | yarn | scar | march | |
| yard | lark | arm | shark | dart | cart | sharp | 108 |

# Drill 15

**āy̸** *(pay)*   **āi̸** *(rain)*   **āi̸+l** *(nail)*

---

| | | | | | | |
|---|---|---|---|---|---|---|
| ray | say | hay | lay | ray | day | |
| may | pay | jay | way | gay | bay | |
| slay | play | clay | flay | clay | pray | 18 |
| bray | tray | gray | fray | pray | clay | |
| may | pay | way | slay | say | day | |
| gay | way | gray | lay | play | gray | 36 |

| | | | | |
|---|---|---|---|---|
| nail | sail | rail | tail | |
| rain | pain | train | chain | |
| paid | laid | maid | gait | 48 |
| may | mail | maid | mail | |
| gray | gay | gait | grain | |
| pay | pain | pail | pray | 60 |

| | | | | | | |
|---|---|---|---|---|---|---|
| say | gain | pray | main | paid | day | |
| nail | may | rain | slay | maid | say | |
| hay | pay | bail | tray | jail | bray | |
| lay | tail | way | laid | clay | tray | 84 |

| | | | | | | | |
|---|---|---|---|---|---|---|---|
| gay | tail | gain | wait | fray | vain | say | |
| jay | gain | fray | bail | way | flay | ray | |
| maid | jay | say | sail | may | slay | day | 105 |
| tray | rain | mail | wait | play | say | pail | |
| bay | play | pail | chain | train | way | say | |
| sail | bray | pain | bait | may | bail | way | 126 |

# Drill 16

**ôr** *(for)*

---

| | | | | | | |
|---|---|---|---|---|---|---|
| h or n | c or n | t or n | b or n | w or n | m or n | |
| s or t | sh or t | f or t | p or t | s or t | p or c h | |
| f or k | c or k | p or k | c or d | f or d | l or d | 18 |

| | | | | | | |
|---|---|---|---|---|---|---|
| f or t | f or d | f or m | f or k | b or n | s or t | |
| c or d | c or n | c or k | c or n | t or n | f or d | |
| p or t | p or k | p or t | p or c h | w or n | h or n | |
| or | f or k | p or k | c or n | b or n | s or t | |
| or b | c or k | h or n | p or t | n or | f or t | 48 |

| | | | | | | |
|---|---|---|---|---|---|---|
| s or t | f or m | c or n | b or n | p or k | l or d | |
| f or k | sh or t | c or k | p or k | f or d | h or n | |
| c or d | w or n | m or n | c or n | s or t | or b | |
| n or | f or | n or | c or d | p or t | p or ch | 72 |

| | | | | | | |
|---|---|---|---|---|---|---|
| sort | nor | fork | lord | short | form | |
| cord | torn | porch | fort | born | morn | |
| torn | horn | cork | sort | or | fort | |
| port | corn | sort | short | born | sport | 96 |

# Drill 17

*ōld*

---

old c old b old t old h old
s old s c old m old g old f old
t old h old old b old c old
f old m old s c old g old s old 20

f old t old b old h old old
b old m old s old g old f old
t old s c old old s old t old
h old c old b old f old m old 40

c old old h old t old m old
s old g old s c old m old h old
t old f old b old c old f old
h old c old t old b old s c old
old h old m old s old g old 65

mold cold hold fold hold scold gold
told hold old sold bold fold scold
hold cold mold told fold gold old
told sold bold hold gold scold gold
mold bold gold cold hold old fold 100

# Drill 18

*ĕ*

---

| | | | | | | |
|---|---|---|---|---|---|---|
| fed | bed | red | Ted | led | bed | |
| beg | bet | bed | leg | let | led | |
| send | lend | bend | tend | fend | send | |
| rest | best | test | pest | crest | nest | |
| west | vest | rent | bent | sent | vent | 30 |

| | | | | |
|---|---|---|---|---|
| fed | send | bed | tend | |
| rest | red | tent | pest | |
| send | bet | best | set | |
| west | best | fend | led | 46 |

| | | | | | | |
|---|---|---|---|---|---|---|
| lend | test | fed | bend | crest | Ed | |
| send | bed | rent | vest | spend | left | |
| red | vent | desk | Ted | west | fed | 64 |

| | | | | | | |
|---|---|---|---|---|---|---|
| rest | bend | set | chest | nest | fed | |
| let | red | Ted | crest | vent | bet | |
| rent | best | send | Ed | spend | led | 82 |

| | | | | | | | |
|---|---|---|---|---|---|---|---|
| west | rest | send | bed | vent | fed | nest | |
| send | let | bed | vest | best | lend | bet | |
| red | beg | bend | test | rent | bent | leg | |
| mend | test | Ed | rest | vent | desk | crest | 110 |

# Drill 19

REVIEW

*är āy̸ āi̸ āi̸+l ôr ōld ĕ*

---

arch hark park card farm lard
say gray clay main tail mail
dart yard mart car charm hard
paid rail chain may play day 24

horn born corn sort fort port
cork fork worn torn short fort
cold mold hold bold told old
send bend tend west crest vest 48

march send park main yard may
may born cart play fort told
mend desk day tail horn pail
dart worn hold charm mold main 72

chest cold chart park fort pail
yard clay train bold charm day
paid gray west tail mold spend 90

desk short day mail farm clay charm
chain fort told dart card vent clay
mart rail corn hold may cork mold
west bold gray hark say fed park 118

# Drill 20

*ā ī ō ū (silent e)*

---

| | | | | | |
|---|---|---|---|---|---|
| bake | bike | broke | bite | hike | |
| came | crime | cove | cute | code | |
| dune | dine | dove | duke | dome | 15 |
| plane | pipe | pose | prune | plate | |
| came | dime | home | fume | huge | |
| base | vise | rose | chase | rise | 30 |

| | | | | |
|---|---|---|---|---|
| fake | gripe | tale | note | |
| hide | coke | doze | tune | |
| stove | take | flake | bride | |
| woke | mute | flute | tote | 46 |

| | | | | | |
|---|---|---|---|---|---|
| bike | fake | note | stove | take | |
| Mike | bike | home | fume | bride | |
| mute | lane | vise | pipe | rose | |
| cape | crime | doze | tune | note | 66 |

| | | | | | | |
|---|---|---|---|---|---|---|
| stove | woke | June | lane | tote | chase | |
| plane | base | prune | flake | home | duke | |
| bake | gripe | tune | tale | fake | cute | |
| cake | crime | doze | mine | came | duke | 90 |

# Drill 21

***ōa̸   ōa̸+l*** *(coal)*

---

**boast boat bloat cloak coach coal**
**coast coat croak goat goal gloat**
**load loaf loan moan moat oat**
**coast soak toad soap boat coast** **24**

**load oat coast soak goat coach**
**boast loaf oak toad poach road**
**roam coal goal coach bloat moan**
**croak soak moan coal oat goat** **48**

**road coach toad goal bloat moan**
**boat cloak soap coal poach coast**
**loaf oak moan moat gloat boat**
**roam goat coach load loan toad** **72**

**load boat toad poach moat coach roam**
**oat coast soak goat coal bloat moan**
**coast loaf croak toad goal loan gloat**
**coach boast load oath cloak goat boat** **100**

# Drill 22

ōw̸ *(low)*

---

blow  row  grow  mow  flow  grown
low  grow  mow  grown  show  own
glow  blow  crow  flown  low  sown
crow  flow  blow  show  snow  throw  24

sown  own  flow  mow  blow  grown
crow  low  flow  grow  flown  blown
shown  mow  blow  show  row  sown
flow  bow  own  sow  glow  blown  48

crow  low  flown  sow  blow  throw
mow  crow  show  grown  row  thrown
glow  own  sow  blow  blown  flown
blow  row  grow  mow  flow  grown  72

grown  row  grow  mow  flow  low  shown
flown  glow  mow  crow  show  snow  grown
low  crow  row  snow  grow  blow  shown
blown  snow  throw  low  flow  low  thrown  100

# Drill 23

***ou*** *(out)*   ***ow*** *(how)*

| | | | | | |
|---|---|---|---|---|---|
| wow | pound | out | loud | round | |
| ouch | shout | spout | couch | mound | |
| proud | grouch | pouch | mouth | ground | |
| found | count | south | cloud | bound | |
| snout | cloud | mount | trout | pouch | 25 |

| | | | | | |
|---|---|---|---|---|---|
| how | bow | cow | vow | down | |
| brow | chow | clown | crowd | frown | |
| gown | owl | now | howl | growl | |
| town | wow | scowl | prowl | brown | 45 |

| | | | | | |
|---|---|---|---|---|---|
| ouch | bow | loud | out | crowd | |
| down | proud | now | mouth | ground | |
| gown | now | south | howl | bound | |
| pouch | count | cow | cloud | clown | 65 |

| | | | | | | |
|---|---|---|---|---|---|---|
| found | owl | south | trout | bound | grouch | |
| crowd | frown | howl | owl | brown | pouch | |
| chow | brow | town | proud | wow | ground | |
| frown | scowl | chow | count | brown | mound | |
| clown | ouch | bow | cow | loud | now | 95 |

# Drill 24

REVIEW

*ā ī ō ū (silent e̸)* *ōa̸* *ou* *ōw̸* *ow*

---

bake stove crime mute home
flow mow show low brow
woke dune mine bride rose
boast croak moan roam poach 20

base rose plane duke pipe
our shout spout mouth loud
how cow crowd frown down
plate brow ouch brown loan 40

chow town stove mute moan
woke boast dune spout crowd
bake mow cake mouth frown
found brow rose bride pouch
brown plate crowd plane croak 65

boast dune show mute home crowd down
our rose croak mine crime show woke
how stove spout frown mouth mow duke
home cake stove rose cow shout bride
chow planc duke brow woke mow pouch 100

# Drill 25

*th wh*

| | | | | | |
|---|---|---|---|---|---|
| thin | theft | thatch | thud | oath | |
| this | that | those | them | fifth | |
| thrash | throb | thrive | throne | growth | |
| thud | thump | path | fifth | theft | |
| growth | oath | with | south | thrash | 25 |

| | | | | | |
|---|---|---|---|---|---|
| whisk | whale | what | wheat | wheel | |
| whirl | wheeze | when | whim | while | |
| wheel | white | whip | whine | white | |
| while | what | wheat | wheel | whale | 45 |

| | | | | | |
|---|---|---|---|---|---|
| this | throb | path | wheel | whale | |
| theft | oath | when | fifth | wheat | |
| white | thud | thump | south | growth | |
| that | those | teeth | with | thrive | 65 |

| | | | | | | |
|---|---|---|---|---|---|---|
| wheel | whip | thud | path | south | that | |
| thump | oath | whim | fifth | wheat | whale | |
| whim | fifth | this | with | oath | that | |
| whine | theft | teeth | white | trash | wheeze | |
| those | while | these | south | fifth | growth | 95 |

# Drill 26

*ng nk*

---

| | | | | | | |
|---|---|---|---|---|---|---|
| bang | bing | bong | bring | clang | cling | |
| clung | fling | ding | dong | dung | gong | |
| hang | hung | king | rung | stung | cling | |
| sing | sang | king | ring | rang | rung | |
| sting | swing | ping | pong | pang | bing | 30 |

| | | | | |
|---|---|---|---|---|
| bank | clink | bunk | blink | |
| honk | hank | drank | drink | |
| drunk | Frank | think | trunk | |
| sink | sunk | slink | spank | 46 |

| | | | | | | |
|---|---|---|---|---|---|---|
| bank | clink | hung | bank | kink | bunk | |
| honk | hang | dung | fling | rink | sang | |
| trunk | prank | pong | ping | king | spring | |
| thing | think | dunk | spank | swing | spunk | 70 |

| | | | | | | |
|---|---|---|---|---|---|---|
| swing | bang | ping | clink | fling | hunk | |
| wink | trunk | sting | honk | sling | ring | |
| honk | clink | drank | think | sang | lung | |
| spunk | sling | stink | tank | sting | king | 94 |

# Drill 27

REVIEW

*th wh ng nk*

---

| | | | | | |
|---|---|---|---|---|---|
| thin | theft | thrive | throne | think | |
| with | growth | path | fifth | teeth | |
| these | that | those | south | thing | |
| wheat | wheel | while | white | when | |
| whale | what | wheeze | whim | wheat | 25 |

| | | | | | |
|---|---|---|---|---|---|
| bang | bring | hung | king | ring | |
| drunk | sank | sink | spank | thank | |
| whip | when | wink | prank | wheel | |
| lung | pong | oath | think | punk | 45 |

| | | | | | |
|---|---|---|---|---|---|
| bank | swing | ping | clink | rink | |
| oath | path | when | wheat | thud | |
| bang | throb | slink | pang | theft | |
| growth | clang | those | thing | thump | 65 |

| | | | | | | |
|---|---|---|---|---|---|---|
| thump | sink | throw | whip | ping | these | |
| growth | wheel | fifth | drunk | path | honk | |
| white | teeth | spunk | theft | sang | them | |
| rang | whale | bring | those | thin | wheeze | |
| oath | lung | wheat | punk | throb | growth | 95 |

# Drill 28

***er*** *(ur – term)* ***ir*** *(ur – fir)* ***ur*** *(ur – turf)*

---

| | | | | | |
|---|---|---|---|---|---|
| birth | jerk | dirt | burn | perk | |
| girl | herb | chirp | burst | fern | |
| curt | fur | shirt | skirt | fir | |
| girl | hurt | stir | swirl | verse | |
| term | perch | sir | flirt | burst | 25 |

| | | | | | |
|---|---|---|---|---|---|
| church | jerk | sir | fern | hurl | |
| stir | perk | burst | sir | flirt | |
| verse | skirt | burn | curb | fir | |
| third | shirt | birth | term | girl | |
| clerk | nurse | serve | turf | bird | 50 |

| | | | | | |
|---|---|---|---|---|---|
| burst | turf | verse | swirl | skirt | |
| stir | jerk | sir | turf | girl | |
| flirt | fern | hurt | term | shirt | |
| stir | church | perch | burn | fern | 70 |

| | | | | | | |
|---|---|---|---|---|---|---|
| girl | pert | dirt | burn | perk | fur | |
| term | chirp | shirt | nurse | serve | sir | |
| dirt | curb | burst | flirt | hurt | verse | |
| clerk | skirt | flirt | term | birth | fir | |
| swirl | third | clerk | turf | bird | curt | 100 |

# Drill 29

***au*** *(ô – cause)* ***aw*** *(ô – paw)*

---

| | | | | | |
|---|---|---|---|---|---|
| haunt | haul | cause | launch | fraud | |
| lawn | paw | raw | slaw | thaw | |
| taut | daub | lawn | caw | yawn | |
| cause | saw | thaw | straw | pause | **20** |

| | | | | | |
|---|---|---|---|---|---|
| crawl | draw | fraud | paw | maul | |
| saw | raw | thaw | yawn | thaw | |
| maul | straw | cause | launch | raw | |
| lawn | paw | haul | daub | straw | |
| caw | pause | gaunt | drawn | haunt | **45** |

| | | | | | |
|---|---|---|---|---|---|
| haul | paw | cause | slaw | lawn | |
| taut | gaunt | raw | fraud | yawn | |
| fraud | caw | lawn | paw | draw | |
| crawl | claw | pause | haul | launch | **65** |

| | | | | | | |
|---|---|---|---|---|---|---|
| haul | cause | launch | raw | haunt | straw | |
| fraud | crawl | paw | pause | saw | law | |
| draw | straw | taut | lawn | slaw | yawn | |
| fraud | raw | maul | yawn | caw | cause | |
| haul | drawn | cause | gaunt | taut | lawn | **95** |

# Drill 30

***ea*** *(ir – ear)* ***ea*** *(ĕ – head)* ***ea*** *(ēa̸ – team)*
***ea*** *(ur – earn)* ***ea*** *(er – wear)*

---

| | | | | | |
|---|---|---|---|---|---|
| please | peach | least | fear | steam | |
| bread | head | dread | lead | thread | |
| heavy | spread | deaf | swear | breath | |
| leaf | team | weak | east | sweat | |
| treat | ready | heart | clean | please | 25 |

| | | | | | |
|---|---|---|---|---|---|
| bear | tear | leak | peak | seat | |
| earth | heard | meant | deaf | dream | |
| mean | read | death | bread | lead | |
| head | tear | wear | clear | rear | 45 |

| | | | | | |
|---|---|---|---|---|---|
| sweat | clear | dear | ear | speak | |
| rear | near | team | east | leaf | |
| please | bear | meant | seam | team | |
| treat | heart | clean | lead | deaf | 65 |

| | | | | | | |
|---|---|---|---|---|---|---|
| weak | sear | meant | ear | dream | near | |
| earth | bear | team | east | treat | clear | |
| please | earth | leak | seat | sweat | thread | |
| earth | please | seam | bread | speak | peach | |
| tear | heart | lead | peak | mean | steam | 95 |

# Drill 31

REVIEW

***er*** *(ur)*   ***ir*** *(ur)*   ***ur***   ***ŏŏ***   ***au*** *(ô)*   ***aw*** *(ô)*

***ea*** *(ir – ear)*   ***ea*** *(e – head)*   ***ea*** *(ēa̸ – team)*   ***ea*** *(ur – earn)*   ***ea*** *(er – wear)*

---

| | | | | | |
|---|---|---|---|---|---|
| **dirt** | **burn** | **perk** | **church** | **verse** | |
| **wool** | **shook** | **poor** | **rook** | **took** | |
| **haul** | **cause** | **launch** | **faun** | **taut** | **15** |
| **sweat** | **clear** | **dear** | **ear** | **speak** | |
| **rear** | **near** | **caw** | **draw** | **crawl** | |
| **peach** | **fear** | **steam** | **treat** | **bread** | **30** |

| | | | | | |
|---|---|---|---|---|---|
| **sweat** | **team** | **book** | **fraud** | **staunch** | |
| **straw** | **deaf** | **thread** | **poor** | **steam** | |
| **crawl** | **good** | **burn** | **meat** | **beach** | **45** |

| | | | | | |
|---|---|---|---|---|---|
| **please** | **peach** | **least** | **fear** | **steam** | |
| **bread** | **head** | **dread** | **lead** | **thread** | |
| **paw** | **straw** | **cause** | **book** | **launch** | |
| **moor** | **cook** | **chirp** | **burst** | **learn** | **65** |

| | | | | | | | |
|---|---|---|---|---|---|---|---|
| hood | dirt | fur | look | straw | launch | please | |
| lawn | treat | straw | shook | took | steam | church | |
| look | draw | verse | purse | cause | pause | thread | |
| thread | burn | beach | haul | perch | church | look | |
| moor | dread | lead | cook | crawl | fraud | speak | 100 |

# Drill 32

***ew** (o͞o – crew)* ***ue** (o͞o – blue)* ***y** (ī – fly)*

---

| | | | | | |
|---|---|---|---|---|---|
| blue | blew | crew | clue | pew | |
| clue | stew | fuel | stew | true | |
| due | hue | flew | drew | cruel | |
| duel | new | stew | mew | clue | 20 |

| | | | | | |
|---|---|---|---|---|---|
| my | dry | by | try | fly | |
| cry | pry | fry | cry | my | |
| clue | pew | try | crew | true | |
| try | by | due | hew | by | |
| drew | fuel | pew | blue | pry | 45 |

| | | | | | |
|---|---|---|---|---|---|
| flew | dry | cruel | stew | cue | |
| blue | Sue | true | fuel | clue | |
| sty | fly | pry | mew | blew | |
| my | cruel | by | duel | try | 65 |

| | | | | | | | |
|---|---|---|---|---|---|---|---|
| my | dry | hew | mew | fry | drew | by | |
| slew | true | try | my | due | fry | dry | |
| pry | stew | blue | clue | true | try | blew | |
| flew | pry | mew | new | stew | sly | by | |
| pew | sty | cruel | fly | flew | my | duel | 100 |

# Drill 33

***oy*** *(ōi – joy)* ***oi*** *(ōi – join)* ***oi+l*** *(ōi+l – oil)*

---

| | | | | | | |
|---|---|---|---|---|---|---|
| **boy** | **joy** | **soy** | **coy** | **toy** | **joy** | |
| **oil** | **spoil** | **soil** | **toil** | **join** | **foil** | |
| **boil** | **coil** | **joy** | **Roy** | **coin** | **point** | |
| **foil** | **toy** | **oil** | **boy** | **spoil** | **soy** | **24** |

| | | | | | | |
|---|---|---|---|---|---|---|
| **moist** | **choice** | **coin** | **oil** | **voice** | **point** | |
| **Roy** | **soy** | **spoil** | **joy** | **coy** | **boil** | |
| **joint** | **foil** | **toy** | **moist** | **boy** | **noise** | |
| **point** | **hoist** | **coil** | **choice** | **coin** | **moist** | **48** |

| | | | | | | |
|---|---|---|---|---|---|---|
| **foil** | **point** | **toy** | **coy** | **spoil** | **choice** | |
| **soy** | **oil** | **hoist** | **voice** | **Roy** | **foil** | |
| **join** | **moist** | **soy** | **toil** | **noise** | **coin** | |
| **boil** | **joy** | **spoil** | **choice** | **toy** | **noise** | **72** |

| | | | | | | | |
|---|---|---|---|---|---|---|---|
| **toy** | **coin** | **join** | **hoist** | **point** | **moist** | **joy** | |
| **toil** | **joy** | **ploy** | **coy** | **foil** | **spoil** | **choice** | |
| **boil** | **soil** | **soy** | **noise** | **boy** | **toy** | **coil** | |
| **hoist** | **foil** | **point** | **Roy** | **coin** | **spoil** | **oil** | **100** |

# Drill 34

***al*** *(ô)*   ***alk*** *(ô)*   ***eigh*** *(ā)*

---

| | | | | | |
|---|---|---|---|---|---|
| ball | walk | fall | hall | Walt | |
| hall | call | stalk | scald | small | |
| bald | walk | tall | talk | chalk | |
| talk | hall | scald | call | small | 20 |
| | | | | | |
| eight | neigh | weigh | weight | freight | |
| sleigh | weigh | neigh | eight | scald | |
| weigh | neigh | freight | sleigh | walk | |
| Walt | stalk | scald | walk | weigh | |
| eight | sleigh | stalk | scald | Walt | 45 |
| | | | | | |
| sleigh | stalk | neigh | call | false | |
| eight | wall | mall | small | weigh | |
| chalk | halt | fall | weight | all | |
| ball | sleigh | wall | eight | fall | 65 |
| | | | | | |
| eight | wall | scald | weight | ball | |
| small | sleigh | walk | neigh | salt | |
| fall | chalk | weigh | stalk | tall | |
| neigh | false | all | eight | bald | |
| chalk | ball | false | wall | freight | 90 |

# Drill 35

REVIEW

***ew*** *(o͞o)* ***ue*** *(o͞o)* ***y*** *(ī)* ***oy*** *(o͞i)* ***ōi***
***al*** *(ô)* ***alk*** *(ô)* ***eigh*** *(ā)*

---

| | | | | | | |
|---|---|---|---|---|---|---|
| blue | crew | mew | clue | stew | fuel | |
| cry | by | try | fry | pry | cry | |
| hall | walk | hall | salt | tall | stalk | |
| eight | weigh | sleigh | weigh | neigh | eight | 30 |

| | | | | | |
|---|---|---|---|---|---|
| fry | stew | sleigh | stalk | all | |
| boy | ball | toy | point | spoil | |
| eight | joint | false | blew | clue | |
| dry | crew | boil | fall | blue | |
| foil | talk | small | sleigh | salt | 55 |

| | | | | | |
|---|---|---|---|---|---|
| mall | small | blue | true | walk | |
| bald | walk | tall | talk | chalk | |
| moist | choice | coin | oil | voice | |
| point | boil | my | try | oil | 75 |

| | | | | | | |
|---|---|---|---|---|---|---|
| joy | hall | eight | stalk | dry | blue | |
| mew | ball | due | spoil | toy | small | |
| new | fry | crew | eight | point | clue | |
| stalk | cry | fuel | false | boy | noise | 99 |

# Drill 36

***c*** *and* ***g*** *followed by* ***e***, ***i***, *or* ***y***   ***dge***

---

| | | | | | |
|---|---|---|---|---|---|
| cell | cent | cite | voice | sauce | |
| gem | mice | gym | choice | page | |
| large | age | wage | face | ice | |
| cent | cite | gem | cell | mice | **20** |

| | | | | | |
|---|---|---|---|---|---|
| fudge | hedge | bridge | edge | ledge | |
| trudge | lodge | judge | badge | dodge | |
| edge | hedge | fudge | bridge | budge | |
| dodge | ledge | trudge | lodge | bridge | |
| edge | budge | hedge | bridge | judge | **45** |

| | | | | | |
|---|---|---|---|---|---|
| place | dodge | cent | judge | lodge | |
| budge | page | ledge | face | badge | |
| ice | age | fudge | cent | cell | |
| mice | cite | voice | sauce | gem | |
| wage | mice | bridge | cite | large | **70** |

| | | | | | | |
|---|---|---|---|---|---|---|
| cell | ice | budge | edge | page | sauce | |
| age | gym | trudge | place | face | dodge | |
| mice | cent | fudge | voice | badge | gem | |
| lodge | germ | bridge | cent | wage | budge | |
| cite | edge | choice | large | page | lodge | **100** |

# Drill 37

SILENT LETTERS

*ph (f)   kn   ck   gh (f)   gh   ght*

---

| | | | | | |
|---|---|---|---|---|---|
| phone | phase | graph | phase | phone | |
| knead | knew | knife | knit | knob | |
| duck | lock | brick | clock | click | |
| chick | knelt | pack | knock | struck | 20 |

| | | | | | |
|---|---|---|---|---|---|
| cough | laugh | rough | tough | cough | |
| light | fight | bright | bought | fright | |
| sight | rough | right | cough | caught | |
| high | thigh | sleigh | sigh | dough | |
| though | high | tough | bought | sleigh | 45 |

| | | | | | |
|---|---|---|---|---|---|
| phone | laugh | knife | bright | peck | |
| chuck | cough | truck | fight | rough | 55 |
| graph | knew | knife | kneel | tack | |
| knock | caught | know | knelt | smack | |
| might | fright | sleigh | knock | weigh | 70 |

| | | | | | | |
|---|---|---|---|---|---|---|
| laugh | chair | cough | tight | peck | chance | |
| kneel | trick | fight | rough | caught | bought | |
| sight | knew | slight | phone | knelt | trick | |
| struck | phase | chick | graph | clock | tight | |
| phase | knead | truck | tough | fight | knight | 100 |

# Drill 38

REVIEW

***c** and **g** followed by **e**, **i**, or y* **dge**

**ph** *(f)* **~~k~~n** **~~c~~k** **~~gh~~** *(f)* **~~gh~~** **~~gh~~t**

---

**cent voice sauce large wage ice**
**lodge judge edge fudge dodge bridge**
**phone phase knee knob choice chance**
**pick track laugh bright fought rough** **24**

**cell place budge page gym trudge**
**phone laugh knife block chirp cough**
**knew tack choice snack sight caught**
**struck lodge know sleigh check badge** **48**

**cough pack knock struck fudge hedge**
**light bright bought fright hedge dough**
**graph high knife kneel bridge edge**
**voice coin ought judge slight city** **72**

**peck choice light phone bridge wage tough**
**smack mice laugh bright lodge gem fought**
**city fright knew place bought trick struck**
**slight page gym phase knife check badge** **100**

# Drill 39

TWO-SYLLABLE WORDS

*Words that end with* ***consonant + y*** *(ē) or* ***y*** *(ē)* ***by itself***

---

| | | | | | |
|---|---|---|---|---|---|
| hap py | pen ny | diz zy | pup py | hob by | |
| mess y | bud dy | jol ly | fuss y | mud dy | |
| bud dy | fuss y | pen ny | sun ny | fun ny | |
| dad dy | jel ly | sil ly | fog gy | chill y | 20 |

| | | | | | |
|---|---|---|---|---|---|
| ba by | fog gy | fus sy | mud dy | par ty | |
| jol ly | dad dy | sil ly | hap py | fun ny | |
| sun ny | jel ly | diz zy | skin ny | mess y | |
| fuzz y | crab by | skin ny | bun ny | par ty | |
| fuss y | mud dy | fog gy | mess y | sil ly | 45 |

| | | | | | |
|---|---|---|---|---|---|
| mud dy | diz zy | fun ny | sun ny | chill y | |
| jol ly | jel ly | mess y | hap py | fog gy | |
| fuzz y | sil ly | pup py | dad dy | bun ny | |
| cra zy | la zy | sass y | grass y | par ty | |
| hap py | hob by | ba by | diz zy | skin ny | 70 |

| | | | | | | |
|---|---|---|---|---|---|---|
| penny | buddy | silly | muddy | bunny | party | |
| fuzzy | messy | fussy | crazy | foggy | buddy | |
| hobby | puppy | jolly | sunny | silly | skinny | |
| happy | penny | dizzy | jelly | penny | crabby | |
| grassy | baby | lazy | chilly | funny | daddy | 100 |

# Drill 40

TWO-SYLLABLE WORDS

*Words that end with* ***'le'*** *(ble, cle, dle, ple, tle, etc.)*

*The 'le' grabs the consonant right before it to form the last syllable.*

| | | | | | | |
|---|---|---|---|---|---|---|
| ta ble | mar ble | sta ble | sad dle | ca ble | bub ble | |
| lit tle | gob ble | sim ple | top ple | sam ple | un cle | |
| bob ble | tem ple | han dle | cat tle | ap ple | a ble | |
| puz zle | pad dle | wig gle | pur ple | mid dle | bub ble | 24 |
| un cle | mud dle | sta ble | bot tle | pur ple | a ble | |
| pud dle | ta ble | ap ple | mid dle | gob ble | jug gle | |
| lit tle | puz zle | jig gle | wig gle | pad dle | mid dle | |
| rat tle | tem ple | han dle | ta ble | cat tle | sam ple | 48 |
| ap ple | gob ble | top ple | un cle | han dle | pur ple | |
| pud dle | puz zle | sam ple | han dle | ta ble | jug gle | |
| tem ple | rat tle | wig gle | sim ple | sam ple | puz zle | |
| cat tle | ap ple | a ble | ta ble | mar ble | sta ble | 72 |
| table | marble | able | sample | apple | handle | |
| puzzle | rattle | little | middle | topple | bottle | |
| gobble | handle | cable | cattle | paddle | middle | |
| juggle | temple | table | paddle | stable | wiggle | 96 |

# Drill 41

REVIEW

*Words that end with* ***'le', consonant + y** (ē), or **y** (ē)* ***by itself***

---

| | | | | | | |
|---|---|---|---|---|---|---|
| **par ty** | **puz zle** | **jug gle** | **mar ble** | **crab by** | **bab ble** | |
| **lit tle** | **la zy** | **gob ble** | **mess y** | **cra zy** | **pup py** | |
| **bob ble** | **tem ple** | **puz zle** | **cat tle** | **ap ple** | **grass y** | |
| **ta ble** | **jug gle** | **rat tle** | **fog gy** | **mid dle** | **bub ble** | **24** |
| **top ple** | **mud dle** | **mid dle** | **bot tle** | **bat tle** | **cop y** | |
| **tab by** | **ta ble** | **bat ty** | **mid dle** | **gob ble** | **jug gle** | |
| **wig gle** | **puz zle** | **jig gle** | **cra zy** | **la zy** | **mid dle** | |
| **pud dle** | **tem ple** | **han dle** | **fuss y** | **cat tle** | **sam ple** | **48** |
| **chill y** | **gob ble** | **top ple** | **un cle** | **jel ly** | **fog gy** | |
| **sam ple** | **puz zle** | **fuzz y** | **han dle** | **grass y** | **jug gle** | |
| **tem ple** | **rat tle** | **wig gle** | **sim ple** | **sam ple** | **puz zle** | |
| **cra zy** | **ap ple** | **a ble** | **bun ny** | **fun ny** | **jol ly** | **72** |

| | | | | | | |
|---|---|---|---|---|---|---|
| **buddy** | **muddy** | **able** | **sample** | **apple** | **marble** | |
| **puppy** | **penny** | **jelly** | **wiggle** | **skinny** | **sunny** | |
| **little** | **stable** | **cable** | **hobby** | **happy** | **middle** | |
| **juggle** | **temple** | **table** | **bunny** | **handle** | **dizzy** | **96** |

# Section 5:

# **Advanced Reading Drills**

# Advanced Drill Directions

## Grades 4 - Adult

Use these advanced drills only upon completion of the basic drills when the student is reading more than 100 words per minute. These advanced drills consist of multi-syllable words with prefixes and suffixes. Because the words are longer, reading speed of the Advanced Drills may decrease in comparison to previous reading drills. Set the mastery goal for each drill after doing the practice read and the initial timed one-minute read.

Upon completion of the Advanced Drills, you can also restart at Drill 1, increasing the words-per-minute goal for mastery. Remember, set the goal after the practice read of the drill and the first timed reading.

## What about Grades 1 - 3?

For Grades 1 - 3, restart the reading drills at Drill 1. Increase the words-per-minute goal for mastery. Remember, set the goal after the practice read of the drill and the first timed reading. Students should be able to read many more words-per-minute the second time around.

## Fluency Rates Tip

The fluency rates of 180 words-per-minute and above are calculated with passages. Every word in a passage is not an advanced word. The advanced reading drills have multi-syllable words, and your fluency rates may decrease in comparison to the previous drills.

## Vocabulary Building Tips

These advanced drills may contain words that your students are unfamiliar with. Be sure to go over definitions of words they are unfamiliar with. You can do this several ways.

- Define the words
- Use the words in a sentence
- Categorize the words
- Think of synonyms for the words
- Think of antonyms of the words
- Make crossword puzzles with the words
- Make word searches with the words, trade and solve them

# Drill 42

SUFFIXES

***ed en es ing***

*The 'ed' suffix has three different sounds:*
*('ed' - needed), ('d' - loved), and ('t' - picked).*

---

| | | | | | |
|---|---|---|---|---|---|
| need ed | paint ed | start ed | wait ed | seat ed | |
| hard en | weak en | bra zen | loos en | strength en | |
| chilled | sailed | loved | seemed | lived | |
| rot ten | swol len | soft en | fast en | length en | |
| shopped | picked | wished | crunched | jumped | 25 |

| | | | | | |
|---|---|---|---|---|---|
| jump ing | fly ing | park ing | camp ing | see ing | |
| toast ed | fixed | de cid ed | stopped | in vit ed | |
| in vit ing | pitched | pitch ing | stripped | shad ing | |
| dish es | lunch es | glass es | bunch es | crash es | 45 |

| | | | | | |
|---|---|---|---|---|---|
| drop ping | plan ning | swim ming | cau tion | rest ing | |
| blend ed | ripped | heat ed | chipped | shad ed | |
| match es | fuss es | cross es | stitch es | strength en | |
| mailed | light en | por tion | asked | blamed | |
| sing ing | need ed | weak en | swol len | loved | |
| soft en | jump ing | de cid ed | men tion | bunch es | 75 |

| | | | | | |
|---|---|---|---|---|---|
| fished | decided | soften | wished | swimming | |
| matches | matches | waiting | shaded | dropping | |
| needed | swollen | jogging | planning | lengthen | |
| resting | flying | asked | lighten | munching | |
| shipped | crosses | waited | mention | strengthen | 100 |

# Drill 43

SUFFIXES

***dom ful less ness sion tion***

---

| | | | | | |
|---|---|---|---|---|---|
| free dom | king dom | wis dom | bore dom | help ful | |
| skill ful | thank ful | aw ful | thought ful | home less | |
| age less | child less | grace less | hope less | good ness | |
| like ness | glad ness | kind ness | na tion | vi sion | |
| ad mis sion | ex pres sion | de ci sion | frac tion | sec tion | 25 |

| | | | | | |
|---|---|---|---|---|---|
| sick ness | king dom | thank ful | bore dom | star dom | |
| com mis sion | wis dom | hope less | free dom | age less | |
| skill ful | per mis sion | ad mis sion | child less | in ter mis sion | |
| good ness | pain ful | harm less | pro fes sion | boast ful | 45 |

| | | | | | |
|---|---|---|---|---|---|
| glad ness | free dom | aw ful | home less | thought ful | |
| help ful | skill ful | wis dom | ad mis sion | sick ness | |
| bore dom | grace less | kind ness | age less | like ness | |
| per mis sion | thank ful | boast ful | de ci sion | trans mis sion | |
| ques tion | fe ar ful | care less | por tion | end less | 70 |

| | | | | | |
|---|---|---|---|---|---|
| wisdom | gladness | childless | awful | thankful | |
| helpful | hopeless | admission | goodness | question | |
| permission | sickness | freedom | kindness | graceful | |
| boredom | skillful | ageless | endless | thoughtful | |
| thankful | fearful | careless | boredom | intermission | |
| harmless | homeless | painful | decision | boastful | 100 |

# Drill 44

SUFFIXES

***acy ant ary ity ive tial***

---

| | | | | | |
|---|---|---|---|---|---|
| con trar y | cus tom ar y | dig ni tar y | sec re tar y | Jan u ar y | |
| no bil i ty | qual it y | char it y | ca pac i ty | sin cer i ty | |
| ir ri tant | col or ant | mil i tant | em i grant | o rig i nal i ty | |
| de moc ra cy | di plo ma cy | lit er a cy | con spir a cy | fi nal i ty | |
| nar ra tive | cool ant | ex ec u tive | talk a tive | punc tu al i ty | 25 |
| priv a cy | vi sion ar y | nar ra tive | cur a tive | a bun dant | |
| im m i grant | ex ec u tive | con trar y | char i ty | punc tu al i ty | |
| con trar y | ac cu ra cy | es sen tial | po ten tial | im par tial | |
| re al i ty | fi nal i ty | dig ni tar y | ac cu ra cy | tech ni cal i ty | |
| sol i tar y | lit er a cy | ac tive | vol un tar y | in struc tive | 50 |
| mil i tar y | char i ty | pros per i ty | im par tial | con struc tive | |
| re al i ty | fi nal i ty | sec re tar y | po ten tial | in flu en tial | |
| de moc ra cy | em i grant | lu na cy | ac cu ra cy | punc tu al i ty | |
| tem po rar y | mil i tant | cus tom ar y | es sen tial | re spon si bil i ty | |
| in struc tive | dig ni tar y | po ten tial | ir ri tant | vol un tar y | 75 |

| | | | | | |
|---|---|---|---|---|---|
| temporary | essential | dignitary | narrative | constructive | |
| reality | talkative | potential | irritant | punctuality | |
| secretary | executive | finality | potential | contrary | |
| reality | abundant | influential | immigrant | technicality | |
| kingdom | accuracy | charity | talkative | influential | 100 |

# Drill 45

REVIEW: SUFFIXES

***acy ary ed en es dom ful less***
***ing ity ness sion tial tion***

---

| | | | | | |
|---|---|---|---|---|---|
| no bil i ty | cus tom ar y | dig ni tar y | sec re tar y | Jan u ar y | |
| stopped | re al i ty | char i ty | pros per i ty | tech ni cal i ty | |
| re al i ty | fi nal i ty | glass es | sin cer i ty | con fi den tial | |
| vi sion | ad mis sion | de ci sion | pro fes sion | punc tu al i ty | |
| con ver sion | por tion | toast ed | plan ning | cus tom ar y | 25 |
| king dom | length en | ques tion | sta tion | res i den tial | |
| po ten tial | in flu en tial | fly ing | char i ty | ad mis sion | |
| con trar y | ad mis sion | lit er a cy | frac tion | in flu en tial | |
| re al i ty | de cid ed | dig ni tar y | de ci sion | tech ni cal i ty | |
| park ing | sin cer i ty | thought ful | free dom | o rig i nal i ty | 50 |
| mil i tar y | harm less | pros per i ty | ques tion | punc tu al i ty | |
| re al i ty | fi nal i ty | sec re tar y | child less | good ness | |
| swim ming | stitch es | de ci sion | pro fes sion | de moc ra cy | |
| wished | ac cu ra cy | vi sion | pain ful | hos pi tal i ty | |
| kind ness | swol len | like ness | in flu en tial | o rig i nal i ty | 75 |

| | | | | | |
|---|---|---|---|---|---|
| potential | fraction | dignitary | parking | needed | |
| hopeless | influential | goodness | question | punctuality | |
| secretary | admission | finality | accuracy | dishes | |
| freedom | decision | essential | strengthen | technicality | |
| accuracy | customary | skillful | residential | influential | 100 |

# Drill 46

PREFIXES

*de dis ex mis non pre re un*

---

| | | | | | |
|---|---|---|---|---|---|
| dis pose | dis hon est | dis a gree | dis cour age | | |
| ex it | ex port | ex pose | ex claim | | |
| re tell | re port | re tract | re tie | | |
| re peat | re turn | re do | re heat | | |
| ex press | dis cov er | dis charge | dis ap pear | | |
| un hap py | un load | un real | un luck y | | 24 |

| | | | | |
|---|---|---|---|---|
| de part | de fine | de fend | de cay | |
| mis take | mis spell | mis treat | mis read | |
| non sense | non fat | non fic tion | pre pare | |
| pre dict | pre re cord | pre tend | pre view | 40 |

| | | | | | |
|---|---|---|---|---|---|
| re wind | dis play | un hap py | ex plain | dis ap pear | |
| non fat | pre view | de fine | un cer tain | un fast en | |
| un luck y | mis di rect | ex cite | mis read | ex tract | |
| non stop | un dress | de lay | dis card | dis hon est | 60 |

| | | | | | |
|---|---|---|---|---|---|
| un hap py | un load | re peat | re turn | ex it | |
| re tell | ex pose | un luck y | ex claim | dis cov er | |
| ex press | de fend | non sense | pre tend | pre view | 75 |

| | | | | | |
|---|---|---|---|---|---|
| discourage | reheat | substitute | unhappy | antifreeze | |
| tricycle | preview | uncertain | nonfat | prepare | |
| submarine | indent | disappear | report | outside | 90 |
| defend | exclaim | retract | disagree | nonsense | |
| prerecord | misspell | expose | misread | unfasten | 100 |

# Drill 47

PREFIXES

***anti auto bi dis in out sub tri***

---

| | | | | | |
|---|---|---|---|---|---|
| an ti bod y | an ti war | an ti freeze | tri cy cle | tri pod | |
| out side | out doors | in dent | in side | in cor rect | |
| sub ma rine | sub tract | sub sti tute | bi ceps | au to mate | |
| dis cour age | pre view | dis cov er | out line | an ti bi ot ic | |
| out field | au to crat | bi coast al | dis own | bi week ly | 25 |

| | | | | | |
|---|---|---|---|---|---|
| au to mat ic | out side | in side | au to mo tive | sub side | |
| tri mes ter | tri pod | dis com fort | in struct or | an ti air craft | |
| sub sist | un a ble | au to ma tion | dis in fect | in grown | |
| dis hon or | in her it | bi fo cals | out line | sub way | |
| out fit | an ti bod y | dis count | in va sive | dis a gree | 50 |

| | | | | |
|---|---|---|---|---|
| an ti bod y | au to mat ic | bi cy cle | dis ap pear | |
| dis ap point | bi plane | au to mo bile | an ti freeze | |
| bi month ly | au to crat | dis lo cate | sub sti tute | 62 |
| dis con tin ue | anti bi ot ic | out pa tient | au to bi og ra phy | |
| bi coast al | au to graph | dis ap pear | in cor rect | |
| tri cy cle | in va lid | bi an nu al | dis ad van tage | 74 |

| | | | | | |
|---|---|---|---|---|---|
| disinfect | biceps | subtract | outline | antibody | |
| bicycle | outline | disappear | bifocals | discover | |
| tripod | indent | substitute | invalid | autograph | 89 |
| discourage | autocrat | discomfort | outpatient | antifreeze | |
| tricycle | invasive | uncertain | automation | subsist | |
| submarine | indent | disappear | antibody | outside | 104 |

# Drill 48

PREFIXES

***ex inter im mid post pro tele trans super***

---

| | | | | | |
|---|---|---|---|---|---|
| ex haust | ex hale | ex it | ex cerpt | ex tract | |
| in ter act | in ter cede | in ter change | in ter com | in ter fere | |
| im ma ture | im pact | im pu ri ty | im mense | im press | |
| mid day | mid life | mid night | mid point | mid day | |
| post card | post war | post date | post age | pro found | |
| pro fess | pro claim | tel e vi sion | tel e scope | tel e vise | 30 |

| | | | | | |
|---|---|---|---|---|---|
| trans port | trans mit | trans fer | trans plant | trans late | |
| su per man | su per vise | pro duc tive | tel e phone | su per nat ur al | |
| tel e scope | pro fit | trans mit | pro ject | su per mar ket | |
| mid sec tion | tel e photo | pro file | im per fect | in ter sec tion | |
| post age | mid night | im mod est | mid town | su per im pose | 55 |

| | | | | | |
|---|---|---|---|---|---|
| im pact | pro fess | ex tra dite | im press | post date | |
| tel e thon | ex hale | im ma ture | mid day | ex tract | |
| in ter cede | im bal ance | pro duc tive | im mense | in ter change | |
| pro duce | trans plant | mid life | post pone | im prop er | |
| trans fer | su per man | mid stream | ex tri cate | tel e vi sion | 80 |

| | | | | | |
|---|---|---|---|---|---|
| midnight | postdate | impolite | superman | impact | |
| profile | telethon | profile | impurity | transplant | |
| transport | interact | telephone | transmit | supernatural | 95 |
| telescope | profit | immature | midpoint | project | |
| telephoto | profile | midday | postcard | interfere | 105 |

# Drill 49

REVIEW: PREFIXES

***anti auto bi de dis ex im inter mid mis***
***non out post pre pro re sub super tele trans un***

---

| | | | | |
|---|---|---|---|---|
| an ti bod y | un hap py | bi cy cle | dis ap pear | |
| re peat | bi plane | au to mo bile | ex port | |
| bi month ly | re tract | dis lo cate | pre re cord | |
| dis con tin ue | ex press | bi coast al | dis charge | |
| an ti bi ot ic | un luck y | an ti air craft | au to bi og ra phy | |
| sub sti tute | de ploy | bi an nu al | dis ad van tage | 24 |

| | | | | |
|---|---|---|---|---|
| post card | mid day | sub side | non sense | |
| de part | mis spell | non f i c tion | im po lite | |
| post script | mid point | im pu ri ty | ex tra dite | |
| im ma ture | un cer tain | non sense | pre re cord | 40 |

| | | | | | |
|---|---|---|---|---|---|
| pro duce | tel e vi sion | re tract | super man | trans plant | |
| out side | trans port | in ter act | pro duc tive | su per im pose | |
| tel e scope | tri cy cle | de cay | pro ject | in ter sec tion | |
| in ter es ting | de fend | un hap py | tel e phone | su per mark et | |
| mid term | out per form | au to mat ic | mis take | out stand ing | |
| pre tend | re peat | sub tract | mid air | ex clude | 70 |

| | | | | | |
|---|---|---|---|---|---|
| disappoint | biplane | automobile | antifreeze | superman | |
| midnight | unload | impolite | submit | outstanding | |
| mistake | preview | nonsense | bicoastal | disadvantage | |
| transport | interact | productive | telephone | supernatural | |
| tricycle | reheat | transmit | project | intersection | |
| defend | profile | uncertain | biplane | postman | 100 |

# Drill 50

MULTI-SYLLABLE WORDS

***Prefixes and Suffixes***

---

| | | | | |
|---|---|---|---|---|
| un beat a ble | o ver flow ing | dis a gree ment | un suc cess ful | |
| re count ed | ex port er | in spect ing | sem i an nu al ly | |
| pro ject or | re duc tion | in ject ed | mis treat ed | |
| pre dic tion | sub scrip tion | o ver re act | de light ful | |
| un clear | trans port | mis for tune | mis un der stand | 20 |

| | | | | |
|---|---|---|---|---|
| tel e vi sion | kind ness | ten der ness | won der ing | |
| care ful ly | help ful | un kind | suc cess ful | |
| pack age | dic tate | pres i dent | per cent age | |
| na tion | sub trac tion | sec re tar y | thought ful ness | |
| in de pen dent | in di rect | in ter act | trans plant | 40 |

| | | | | |
|---|---|---|---|---|
| kind ness | o ver flow ing | ten der ness | de light ful | |
| un beat a ble | in ject ed | thought ful ly | help ful | |
| per cent age | care ful ly | o ver load | won der ing | |
| in flu en tial | con fi den tial | de fense | ex press | |
| help ful | dic tate | sec re tar y | sub scrip tion | 60 |

| | | | | | |
|---|---|---|---|---|---|
| subscription | overload | inspecting | defense | semiannually | |
| unsuccessful | projector | unbeatable | percentage | thoughtfully | |
| recounted | dictate | defense | indirect | percentage | 75 |
| injected | carefully | delightful | overreact | misunderstand | |
| nation | reduction | unkind | interact | thoughtfulness | |
| prediction | tenderness | mistreated | package | overflowing | |
| subtraction | kindness | injected | unbeatable | disagreement | 95 |

# Drill 51

MORE MULTI-SYLLABLE WORDS

***Prefixes and Suffixes***

| | | | | | |
|---|---|---|---|---|---|
| ex claim | tri cy cle | re duc tion | de fend | o ver flow ing | |
| po ten tial | in flu en tial | pre pare | dis mis sive | dis a bil i ty | |
| sub tract | tri pod | un hap py | mis spell | per mis sion | |
| de light ful | in ject ed | ex claim | tri cy cle | sub ma rine | |
| pro jec tor | mid point | pre view | care ful ly | an ti freeze | |
| de part | im pur i ty | sec re tar y | ex tra dite | ex tra sen so ry | 30 |

| | | | | |
|---|---|---|---|---|
| pro jec tor | re duc tion | in ject ed | mis treat ed | |
| un beat a ble | o ver flow ing | ex port er | re duc tion | |
| pre dic tion | dis count ed | ten der ness | won der ing | |
| per cent age | care ful ly | in spect ing | de light ful | |
| in side | ex port er | non fic tion | sem i an nu al ly | 50 |

| | | | | |
|---|---|---|---|---|
| dis a gree | dis hon est | help ful | dis cour age | |
| un beat a ble | in ject ed | o ver re act | sem i an nu al ly | |
| sub way | an ti freeze | li brar y | dis a gree ment | |
| out side | post script | in dent | dis in ter est ed | |
| dis pose | un load | im po lite | ex tra or di nar y | |
| pro jec tor | mis hap | an ti bod y | re duc tion | 74 |

| | | | | | |
|---|---|---|---|---|---|
| prediction | injected | unbeatable | percentage | subscription | |
| mistake | prepare | antibody | submarine | thoughtfulness | |
| permission | carefully | mistreated | tenderness | disability | |
| delightful | unbeatable | unload | dispose | percentage | 94 |
| repellent | inspecting | impolite | exporter | unsuccessful | |
| prediction | tripod | overflow | reality | semiannually | 104 |

# Drill 52

FINAL REVIEW

***Prefixes and Suffixes***

| | | | | | |
|---|---|---|---|---|---|
| telephone | permission | automobile | biplane | antifreeze | |
| midnight | unload | impolite | dismissive | extracurricular | |
| disaster | preview | profile | mistake | disadvantage | |
| transport | interact | productive | disappoint | supernatural | 20 |
| subscription | profile | inspecting | defense | semiannually | |
| unsuccessful | projector | unbeatable | percentage | thoughtfully | |
| recounted | dictate | defense | indirect | percentage | |
| bicoastal | carefully | delightful | unload | misunderstand | 40 |
| nation | reduction | unkind | interact | thoughtfulness | |
| prediction | tenderness | mistreated | reduction | overflowing | |
| subtraction | kindness | injected | unbeatable | disagreement | 55 |
| prediction | injected | unbeatable | percentage | subscription | |
| mistake | prepare | antibody | submarine | thoughtfulness | |
| outdoors | carefully | mistreated | tenderness | disability | |
| delightful | unbeatable | unload | dispose | percentage | 75 |
| midnight | inspecting | impolite | exporter | unsuccessful | |
| dictate | projector | nonfat | overflowing | preview | |
| prediction | nonsense | tripod | reality | semiannually | 90 |
| outdoors | overflowing | mistreated | tenderness | subscription | |
| subscription | unbeatable | semiannually | disability | thoughtfulness | |
| delightful | inspecting | percentage | unsuccessful | disagreement | 105 |
| percentage | dictate | projector | carefully | thoughtfulness | |
| prediction | overflowing | inspecting | extrasensory | unsuccessful | 115 |

# Works Cited

Bashir and Hook. "Fluency: A Key Link between Word Identification and Comprehension." Language, Speech, and Hearing Services in Schools. 2009, http://lshss.pubs.asha.org/article.aspx?articleid=1782754

Chard, D., Tyler, R., and Vaughn, S. "A Synthesis of Research on Effective Interventions for Building Reading Fluency with Elementary Students with Learning Disabilities." Journal of Learning Disabilities. 2002, http://journals.sagepub.com/doi/abs/10.1177/00222194020350050101

Harris & Sipay, Hasbrouck & Tindal, Manzo, and Rasinski. "Fluency Standards Table." Reading A-Z. 2018, https://www.readinga-z.com/fluency/fluency-standards-table/

Wilson, Dr. Debra, S'Cool Moves for Learning. Integrated Learner Press, 2000

Hudson, R., Lane, H., and Pullen, P. "Reading Fluency Assessment and Instruction: What, Why, and How?" http://www.fcrr.org/publications/publicationspdffiles/hudson_lane_pullen_readingfluency_2005.pdf

Mercer, Campbell, et. al. "Effects of a Reading Fluency Intervention for Middle Schoolers With Specific Learning Disabilities." Learning Disabilities Research & Practice, vol. 15. no. 4, 2010, Pp. 179-189. http://www.tandfonline.com/doi/abs/10.1207/SLDRP1504_2

Moats, Louisa. "Whole-Language High Jinks: How to Tell When "Scientifically-Based Reading Instruction" Isn't." 2007, https://edex.s3-us-west-2.amazonaws.com/publication/pdfs/Moats2007_7

Palmer, Mary. "The Relationship Between Reading Fluency, Writing Fluency, and Reading Comprehension in Suburban Third-Grade Students." 2010, ERIC. https://eric.ed.gov/?id=ED522191

Rasinski, T., "What Research Says About Reading, Creating Fluent Readers." Educational Leadership. vol. 61. no. 6. 2004, Pp. 46-51. http://www.ascd.org/publications/educational-leadership/mar04/vol61/num06/Creating-Fluent-Readers.aspx

Schumaker J.B., Deshler D.D. "Validation of Learning Strategy Interventions for Students with Learning Disabilities: Results of a Programmatic Research Effort." In: Wong B.Y.L. (eds) Contemporary Intervention Research in Learning Disabilities. Disorders of Human Learning, Behavior, and Communication, 1992, Springer, New York, NY https://link.springer.com/chapter/10.1007/978-1-4612-2786-1_2

Shaywitz, S., Overcoming Dyslexia. Vintage Books, A Division of Random House, Inc. New York, 2003

Taylor, J., Davis, M., & Rastle, K. (2017). "Comparing and validating methods of reading instruction using behavioural and neural findings in an artificial orthography." Journal of Experimental Psychology: General, Pp. 1-34. DOI: 10.1037/xge0000301 https://pure.royalholloway.ac.uk/portal/en/publications/comparing-and-validating-methods-of-reading-instruction-using-behavioural-and-neural-findings-in-an-artificial-orthography(11dc627f-1ea3-4e1e-9048-0928c0ff2e38).html

Terry, B. "Reading Fluency Research." Bonnie Terry Learning. 2016. https://bonnieterrylearning.com/research/reading/fluency/

Terry, B. "Reading Fluency Gain." Bonnie Terry Learning. 2014. https://bonnieterrylearning.com/product/improve-reading-fluency-speed-help/